What happens when a man is struck down by a terminal case of Cricket Fever? How does he square this condition with the demands of normal life?

The answer might be to become a schoolmaster: gentle mornings of chalk and talk, followed by endless afternoons on the cricket pitch ...

Chasing Balloons recounts Mark Floyer's journey from boy to geriatric, through the classrooms and cricket grounds of Middle England, in pursuit of the perfect cover drive.

Mark Floyer is a teacher, poet and amateur cricketer. He lives in rural West Devon with his wife Snezzy, four dogs, six cats and a shed full of Wisdens.

CHASING BALLOONS

Footnotes of a cricket tragic

Mark Floyer

CHARLCOMBE BOOKS

Charlcombe Books
17 George's Road, Bath BA1 6EY
01225 335813

First published 2019

ISBN: 978 1 9996558 7 7

Printed and bound in Great Britain by
CPI Antony Rowe, Chippenham, Wilts

A moment of reckoning with Father Time

It's Sunday morning. Every limb of my body is aching. I can barely drag my body out of bed to let the dogs out for a pee. What could I possibly have done to deserve this early premonition of geriatric meltdown? I only sank one beer last night ...

Cricket ... yes, I played cricket yesterday afternoon for the Grayshott 3rd XI against Peper Harrow on a quintessentially fine late July day on a quintessential 'cradle of cricket' ground at Lurgashall in Sussex where vintage cars deposit gilded city suburbanites for a slice of Home Counties gastropub fare at the Noah's Ark. I didn't bowl, I didn't bat, my fielding was indifferent and I got hooked up in a trivial dispute with an opposition bowler over the back-foot no-ball law when I was doing my stint as umpire.

I'm sixty years old. I have been footling about with this absurd and addictive game for over fifty years. These days my fielding is so abject that I need to be hidden in the slips in the hope that no batsman will snick it my way; my bowling (while I foolishly imagine that I can sling the ball onto the deck like the legendary Aussie quick Tommo at his best) is only required if the game has run into the doldrums and the captain spots a chance to 'indulge' the old boy; my batting ... well, I can't see as well anymore and my reactions are slower ... but that's OK. At least I play straight, though like my seven-year-old self who first picked up willow, I can't seem to hit the damn ball off the square these days.

The season is approaching its autumn. I can look back on the usual catalogue of false hopes and dashed outcomes, matches cancelled through weather or absenteeism, catches fumbled and balls played and missed. Somewhere, however, in the replay sequence in my head is one moment when I picked a line, placed my feet correctly, stroked through and felt the satisfying thud of leather on willow as the ball bisected the field and cruised to the boundary edge. I felt good – I felt young! My internal cinema erased a season's worth of clumsy swipes to leg, and once again I was the star of my private home video.

I ought to retire at the end of this season. Or rather, just not be around for the spring nets in February. No-one will miss me. I've spent my whole life suddenly 'not being there'. I imagine my death will occur with similar Beckettian absence of significance. Floyer? Who? I was never really 'there' in the first place, just practising perfect solitary cover drives on the far boundary. Will I miss it? ... Will I ever!? You can be sure that long before the first early season mow of the pitch I shall be dusting down my cricket kit and plotting my return to the crease.

Early years in Calcutta

So, where did it all begin?

Ballygunge Park Road, Calcutta 1962. Wisden, the bible cherished by all cricket tragics, informs me that between 30 December 1961 and 4 January 1962 India beat England at Eden Gardens by 187 runs, a surprising result against the grain of early India vs England matches – but no longer the case! What was I doing then? Zoom the lens on a six-year-old boy living in a magnificently dilapidated old wreck of a Company house on Ballygunge Park Road.

Which parent gave me the cricket tragic gene?

My parents' marriage had hit the rocks. My mother, pregnant with my brother James, had fallen in love with a Frenchman whom she would later marry. My father, who was usually absent working on pipeline construction up in Assam, must have been back in the city. A screen memory captures him going out of his mind, chasing his rival through the streets of Calcutta in a taxi brandishing an axe shouting: "Jaldi, Driver, Jaldi!" All very

Anna Karenina – though, of course, that was par for the course in the adult world, and I hadn't been following the cricket at Eden Gardens because cricket was still a mystery to me. Instead, I lay in bed behind my protective gauze netting, rhythmically running a Dinky toy up and down the sheets while I listened to the crows croaking as dusk fell outside my window.

At some point that year I was dropped off at a cricket coaching starter class for young English boys. I can remember sitting in a line on a humid morning by a corner of the Maidan having to listen to an adult coach drone on whilst he illustrated a repetitive lurch of foot and bat which he called a 'forward defensive'. In the background stood the shimmering white megafice of the Victoria Memorial with its statue of a moody old Queen Victoria presiding over her lost Empire. Somehow the coaching session and her presence were connected ... forward or defend? I was bored and disconnected but, as usual, anxious not to betray any of these symptoms. I'd have preferred to be at Tollygunge riding my pony or ploughing up and down the pool at the swimming club, anything but this tedium; the potential enchantment of willow and leather quite passed me by. It was not until April 2015 that I finally made it to the Eden Gardens ground where my daughter Olivia and I saw a frenetic IPL game between the Kolkata Knight Riders and the Bangalore Royal Challengers, during which the West Indian opener Chris Gayle bludgeoned a succession of sumptuous sixes into the far reaches of the stands to the accompaniment of hysterical applause from the crowd.

Prep School years

April 1963 and I was in England, poised to start my prep school life at St Michael's School in North Devon. My father and I had travelled from India and over Easter we enjoyed a series of palliative father-and-son bonding mini-breaks, firstly skiing in the Austrian resort of Lech and then exploring the Thames upriver in a motor cruiser. We had popped into Billings and Edmonds to finalise my trunk load of uniform – including white shirts for cricket, cap with school insignia and the classic 'Lord of the Flies' snake-clasp belt worn by every prep school boy during the 1950s and 60s – and then set off west down the A30 to Cornwall for a few days of 'acclimatisation'. That winter had been the notorious one of 62/63 when the country froze to a standstill. I can recall seeing huge drifts of snow banked on either side of the A30 on Bodmin Moor as we journeyed down to Falmouth.

Driving through the gates of St Michael's School was like entering Dante's first circle of Hell, and the parting from my father can still make a lump rise in my gorge fifty years on. Was this how childhood ended and a British boyhood began? My upper lip fought a desire to quiver as it froze dutifully into a stiff carapace of resolve. First Commandment: "Thou shalt not blub before thy father!"

St Michael's was (and is, though the school was shut down in 2012 due to financial difficulties) a beautiful large villa set in abundant grounds overlooking Codden Hill and the Taw Valley. The unique micro-climate of North Devon – rain and mild temperatures – makes it particularly lush so that the foliage is almost luminescent in its greenness. (No, I wasn't on the homebrew then or now as I recollect! I've been back a few times and the greenness remains strikingly luminescent on each return!) If the school day had not been punctuated with bells, lessons, pecking orders and all the irksome accompaniments of institutional life, this would have been paradise. There was no child protection legislation in place in those days, and we schoolboys were free to roam the grounds like wild creatures, dodging the dubious advances of our prep-school teachers, who were similarly unfettered and licensed to indulge playful peccadilloes of paedophile fetish on our young bodies and minds (not entirely joking!).

The headmaster was a charismatic charmer called Cecil Cook who, apart from a balding pate, looked and behaved with the perfect manners of an early David Niven. An Old Pauline, in his youth he had been a dashing amateur sportsman and socialite much sought after on the debutante scene of his generation. However, the prospect of growing up, donning a city suit and developing a paunch didn't attract him, so he married a rich deb and ploughed her money into buying a school where he could be Head Boy all his life and continue to practise his cricket. Facetious tone aside, he was a naturally gifted schoolteacher who ran the school as a kind of benevolent autocracy. When he died two years later at the untimely early age of 58, the whole school went into protracted mourning at the loss of a very special individual. However, as my father drove away from the school gates on that first day and I promised him not to 'blub', the unique qualities of my future substitute paterfamilias were the least of my concerns. I was paired up with a boy slightly older than me, told that my new identity was number nine and sent off to be inducted into the rituals of this brave new world ...

I don't have many memories of the next three months of the summer term. I think I must have been in a state of catatonic misery which has erased all records from my recall. My letters home – we had to sit and compose a letter home after church on Sunday mornings – give no clues as to my state of mind. My letters home ran as follows:

> dear mummy and daddy,
> i hope you are well. i am fine.
> love number nine.

which translates as code for: "Dear mummy and daddy, I am suicidally depressed but realise that English boys don't express their feelings. When can I be released from this prison? Love Mark."

I was clearly a cause for concern, however, to my new form mistress, Miss Milton. Alarmed at my state of permanent withdrawal from my peers, she alerted the headmaster, who subsequently penned my father an extraordinary letter opening (as letters from one 'chap' to another did in those days) "My dear Floyer". In this letter, he gave a précis of Miss Milton's observations and added: "for it would appear from this that he might be unhappy." However, with breezy sang-froid, he went on to refute this by adding "I do not think this is so" and quickly assured my father that "I would hazard a guess that when he does lose any tension he is going to be a pretty good naughty boy." In a postscript, he appended: "I take the bottom form for nets, and also mark him down as a potential cricketer." Later in the term he further reassured my father as to my innate qualities of British phlegmatism: "After the end of his last boxing lesson I saw him in tears. When I asked him what was the matter he said it was not because someone had hit him but because he couldn't get his gloves off. He is a good little boy and is going to do well." Translation in code: it's OK, Floyer, put aside your concerns, your boy is developing a splendid stiff upper lip!

Ah! that first recognition of one cricket tragic for another! And Oh! how I have been an addict of net practice ever since, seeking out the most bizarre opportunities to 'turn an arm'! Cecil Cook had been in the St Paul's XI for two years and later played for Devon. As he coaxed me to 'front foot forward ... play!' with loving zealotry, I felt the key to the gates of cricketing joy turn just slightly. Yes, if I could one day emulate my new heroes of the St Michael's 1st XI and locate the path from 'Inferno' through 'Purgatorio', then I would surely join the 'Paradiso' of the Gods.

Everyone was cricket crazy at St Michael's. When we weren't in the nets or rolling each other out with pea-shooters in our endless afternoon games periods up at the pitches, we were playing French cricket or throwing balls into the catching cradle. Every week we had to berth our bats in the cricket

St Michael's 1st XI, 1968

lockers so that Bert the odd job man could oil them. Bert was a North Devon troglodyte with colourfully tattooed forearms who tacked his ample girth in with a wrestler's belt. He lived in a shed on site where he stashed his booze and his porn, and whenever he emerged to do an 'odd job' he would growl at us in a broad Devonian accent: "Orr roight!" Despite these somewhat alarming Neanderthal credentials, he was a wonderful bat-oiler and after one of his sessions the smell of linseed oil would mix deliciously with the freshly mown grass to produce a heady summer concoction which wafted down the school corridors. Our bats were our treasures and we chose them for the Test match cricketers who had autographed them: the elegant Peter May, the imperious Colin Cowdrey, dashing 'Lord Ted' Dexter, stylish Tom Graveney, belligerent Ken Barrington and the doughty run-accumulator John Edrich (runs, I learnt later, not being the only commodity he accumulated!). With schoolboyish glee we were convinced that just fondling these bats in our palms would start the process of transformation from boy to Test hero.

Indoors we played endless rounds of Howzat, a game played with two dice which covered all the possibilities of outcome in which you chose teams to compete against each other in imaginary contests. The teams usually comprised of myself, a few mates (when I acquired some) and a sprinkling of Test stars to make up the numbers. These games mimicked the timeless Test match between England and South Africa in 1939 and would continue through lesson time hidden under cover of our desks and late at night by torchlight under bed covers. The only problem was that the No 11 batsman – someone like lugubrious Fred Rumsey – often outscored the specialist batsmen up the order. Another game we played endlessly was Dot Cricket. Here you made up a chart which spread the various permutations of the game across a sheet of paper. You then closed your eyes and prodded a pencil tip randomly into the sheet and whatever you landed on was your result: a miss of any outcome at all was a dot ball. This game simulated the vagaries of cricket much more closely than Howzat, though when MA Floyer came into bat in the Third Test at Lords a subliminal force would miraculously direct the nib towards a succession of fours and sixes. The best way to get your own back on a fellow pupil who had annoyed you was to condemn them to a miserable series of low scores – a kind of prep-school version of voodoo dolls.

My father first really became acquainted with my gathering obsession with cricket the following summer. During his parental turn to look after me during the summer break of 1964, he based us at Cawsand, on the Cornish side of the River Tamar. Here he could pursue his hobby of dinghy racing while simultaneously supervising my holiday from St Michael's. It was the summer of the 1964 Ashes series, and 'The House of the Rising Sun' by the Animals hit number one in the charts in July. My day would begin at breakfast in our hotel with the sports pages of the Daily Telegraph so that I could pore over the minutiae of the previous day's county scoreboards. Whilst my father set off to sail his hired dinghy off the Cornish coast, I'd hole up in the hotel room and listen to the Test Match commentary on the radio, marvelling as Bobby Simpson accumulated his mammoth 311 and retained the Ashes for Australia. Next summer in 1965 we were back in Cornwall where my father completed purchase and took possession of a cottage near the Helford Passage and I persuaded him to erect a cricket net in the garden. He must have rued the day that he agreed to indulge my hobby as I was relentless in dragging him out to bowl over after over at me – not easily done as his right arm was crooked from a war wound in which he had been shot by a Japanese sniper in the Malaysia campaign of 1945.

My father was a very keen sportsman, but cricket was never his game. That said, he always had one over me with his tale (apocryphal or not!) of the six he once hit at Lord's. The story he told was that before de-mobilisation from the Army in 1946 he attended a Services match between the Army and the Navy held on the hallowed turf in St John's Wood. On the day the Army found themselves one man short so my father volunteered himself from the crowd of spectators to make up the numbers. When the Navy fast bowler sprinted in (a composite of Larwood, Lindwall and Miller supposedly!) to unleash a thunderbolt at the non-cricketing volunteer number 11, my father whirled his bat blindly and top-edged a six into the stands!

1964 and 1965 were a blur of Beatles and cricket. Most of my holidays were spent with great friends of my parents, John and Ruth Glen. Ruth was like a second mother to me, greeting me and my trunk on the platform at Waterloo at the end of each term and putting me up in their flat in Hampstead with her two boys of similar age to me, Doug and Dave. We boys were Beatle mad, wore Beatle wigs and avidly collected Beatles pictures in bubble gum packets. I can still feel the anticipation as we lowered the stylus on to the record and heard that brief crackle of static before the opening chord of 'A Hard Day's Night' chimed, a cue for us to twist and shout with cricket bats as guitars in our hands. I was always Paul, fancying myself as the soulful melody maker whilst Dave saw himself as the more abrasive John. Doug, two years younger, was forced to be Ringo as we needed a drummer whilst George was callously dropped from the set list. We even attended a Beatles concert at Hammersmith Odeon where we endured a backing band called the Yardbirds fronted by a guitar genius called Eric Clapton before failing to hear a note as The Beatles tried to play a set over a barrage of hysterically screaming teenagers. Recently I chanced upon a letter I wrote back to Calcutta during one of my London-based Glen holidays which included my first venture into verse: the subject, the Beatles of course! It's worth quoting in full, complete with juvenile spelling, for its sublimely innocent surreality. I suspect that I have failed to improve in a lifetime of scribbling verse since ...

> I have a tale so sad to tell
> I'm to upset to tell it well
> About my Beatle book don't laugh
> I was reading in the Bath.
> I slipped and they fell out of sight.
> And now it looked a sorry sight.
> George is shrivelled Pauls suit is shrunk.
> I think that John should do a bunk.
> His hair is straggley his coat is soked
> And poor Ringo nearly choked
> I tried but in vain
> They looked as if there been in rain.
> I suppose I shall have to buy another
> If I can have some money from Mother.

More successful was my first trip to Lord's in summer 1965 when England were playing South Africa. I can still remember Fred Rumsey's long run-up from the boundary rope as he huffed and puffed up, staggered to the crease and then let a beer-belly wrenching delivery fly from a blender of whirling limbs. Which was better – to see Paul McCartney or Fred Rumsey in the flesh? I was spoilt for choice.

Meanwhile my cricket career at St Michael's was developing auspiciously. It helped that St Michael's was a small school which had about fifteen boys in each year group, so that making the team cut was hardly difficult; indeed, you had to have a pretty good excuse to dodge team selection and escape the weekly ignominy of drubbings at the hands of larger prep schools like Wolborough Hill in Newton Abbott (alma mater of the Devon and England cricketing Tolchard brothers). Defeat can become quite an addiction, and I relished moments when I came to the crease and top-scored with six runs or took the solitary wicket with an analysis of 3-0-41-1, or flukily stopped a near certain boundary at cover point thwacked by one of the afore-mentioned Tolchard brothers. On reflection, I've never really learnt how to win: coming second is addictively bitter sweet.

1966 brought the West Indies and the great Gary Sobers to England. Up to now, my cricket exposure had been a distinctly 'waspy' affair. These athletic black cricketers from the calypso beaches of rum and reggae brought a freedom of expression to the game which quite took your breath away: the sheer pace of Hall and Griffith, the rhythmical offspin of Lance Gibbs, the mercurial and inventive stroke-making of Rohan Kanhai. Over and above these demi-gods, the magician Sobers presided like a nonchalant Prospero. With languorous left-handed ease he could caress the ball all over the field and then suddenly unleash a barrage of brutal hits (as the Glamorgan trundler Malcolm Nash was to discover one day in 1968 at Swansea). As a bowler, he switched from left-arm fast to back-of-the-hand chinamen as the game dictated and he snaffled chances in the slips like a panther. By contrast, good old Geoffrey Boycott with his orthodox 'Yerkshire grit' seemed about as appetising as the semolina junket we were served up as pudding at school.

Upon entering my last years at St Michael's, two factors started to loom over the idyll of non-stop cricket: Common Entrance and puberty. The first necessitated the altogether unfair but not wholly undeserved apartheid of dividing the Scholarship set from the Common Entrance plodders. I found myself in the latter whilst the nerds like Hastings-Smith and Grenville II who couldn't play cricket for toffee started to flaunt their destined futures at Winchester and Eton with insouciant hauteur. For the plodders like me, however, a sword of Damocles hovered from above. To gain entrance to a school like Sherborne you had to achieve 60% in the core subjects of Maths, English and Latin. Blundell's would take you on 55%, and then in descending order you might look to Allhallows, Milton Abbey, Monkton Combe et alia. And if you were 'really thick' (the thickoes included a lot of dyslexics – in those days dyslexics didn't officially 'exist' and had to suffer all manner of excruciating humiliation throughout their schooling life before being released into the world where they duly became entrepreneurial wizards like Richard Branson and left the Classical scholars to dutifully slog through Oxford and the Foreign Office), your parents might give up on you and dump you at the local secondary mod ... ooh aargh! 'morph' into Bert the odd job man! The days of dreamily staring through the classroom window had to stop in lessons, or else ...! The second development was the worrying shift in our physiognomies. Some of us, like me, retained all the trappings of pre-pubescent innocence as we approached our teens, whilst others started to croak and grow patchy tufts of hair in strange places. Our nightly 'rolls' with each other in the dormitory after Lights Out began to display disturbing qualities of emergent sexual awareness. Young bodies got smellier and harder and an embarrassed caustic humour masked the changes we were reluctant to acknowledge. Likewise, the weekly rough-and-tumble tickle sessions with our Geography teacher on Sunday evenings – in which he bartered an evening of Cocoa and watching Harry Worth on TV for a group grope on his couch – left us feeling less than wholesome about what had been exchanged. References to that previously despised species 'Woman' proliferated in our conversations as we swapped allegiances for our Test heroes (well, not entirely ...) to sudden 'pashes' for pouting temptresses like Julie Christie, Brigitte Bardot and Raquel Welch. My 'pash' was for the gamin Mia Farrow whose subtle mix of sexuality and vulnerability appealed to my nascent fascination and squeamishness about this troubling new agenda looming over me ... Sex.

Masturbation was the new obsession. At night, knees would furtively prop up bedcovers and a sibilant frottage of rustling sheets would break out in different zones of the dorm. We ambushed each other in 'flagrante delicto' and de-bagged the victim to check if his member was stiff or limp. In class there was a backrow Wankers Club where with right hand above desk busy writing notes and left hand clasping penis through a cut out hole in the trouser pocket (or vice versa for left-handers) we strove to outdo each other in feats of covert self-abuse; a steady engine room of thud-thud rhythmic juddering jostled for attention with the droning monologue from the teacher at the blackboard. Little did we know that when Miss Milton would regularly interrupt Mr Saville's Maths lesson five minutes before the bell and engage him with lewdly contorted finger hieroglyphics, the teachers might be indulging in games of their own!

Of course, we didn't have ready access, like today's youngsters, to hardcore porn on our mobile phones. One day Pinkerton smuggled in a copy of 'Titbits', a magazine which interspersed humdrum gossip stories with picture profiles of pimply semi-clad young models, who were clearly amateurs moonlighting from their 9-to-5 jobs. In the days before Laker transported British flesh to the Spanish Costas for an annual roasting, English skin was pallid and doughy as a puff pastry left out overnight, and just as unappetising. 'Mandy, 34-26-34, working at the Wimpy Bar in Basingstoke, hopes to become a secretary and meet the man of her dreams' was a typical item, while the next issue promised 'Swedish delights' which had us chortling about the swedes grown in the school kitchen gardens and served up to us at mealtimes. 'Parade' proved a little bit raunchier but the most lurid stories were improbably filtered through the newspapers which were ordered into the library to increase our current affairs awareness; a defensive legal system, still reeling from the Lady Chatterley ban and the Profumo scandal, was now hurtling into the swinging sixties of Carnaby Street, marijuana busts on rock stars like The Stones and naked hippies turning on and tuning in during the summer of love in San Francisco.

Despite the attractions of Mandy in 'Titbits' and our peeping tom expeditions into the sand dunes at Saunton Sands to try and catch two pasty-faced trippers swaddled in mackintoshes and blankets 'at it', real sex was Larkinesque in its elusiveness: 'Sexual intercourse began/ In nineteen sixty-three/ (which was rather late for me) –/ Between the end of the "Chatterley" ban/ And the Beatles' first LP.' In the meantime we were left with our own agonising confusion over this early surge of testosterone ... and, of course, the sustaining charms of cricket.

I spent my last two summer terms playing for the 1st XI, a modest triumph of which I was enormously proud. We gravitated from wearing dinky little shorts to proper whites, school blazer and cap, and set off in the school mini-bus to represent the school against mighty Devon prep school rivals such as Mount House near Tavistock. Despite regular thrashings, we would return to the school as heroes and little nippers (younger years) would listen with bated breath to our descriptions of giant fast bowlers hurling the ball past our ears. The highlight of the season was the Old Boys Weekend when a team of alumni took on the 1st XI. As a handicap, the adults had to bat with a shaved splice of a bat and the game was always manufactured into a tie before the old boys retreated to a booze-up in the headmaster's study; later, when the party was over, we boys would creep cat-like into the study and lick out any remains of ale left in the pewter mugs strewed across the floor. This was our first induction into the potent combination of cricket and alcohol, best approached with caution. One or two pints of golden nectar at a cricket ground of choice – say, Worcester or Hove – with a Wisden tucked under the arm watching a sleepy game of county cricket is the nearest a man can approach heaven. More than two pints, however, turns into nine or ten and leads him into an alcoholic hell, blabbering or blubbering about the day he nearly scored a fifty for The Erratics against Zeal Monachorum back in the day to any fellow barstool drunk prepared to listen. That summer I also won the treasured silver Batting Bat for scoring the most runs for the 1st XI and set my sights on a Test Match career.

With all this excitement on the cricket pitch, my studies had kept a low profile and it was decided that I should stay on a term and see if I could pump up my chances of making that 60% percentage required by Sherborne school for Common Entrance. My contemporaries had moved on to their respective public schools so I was made Head Boy and for the only time in my life held a position of responsibility with some semblance of credibility. For three brief months I feigned possession of the natural authority of Ralph in 'Lord of the Flies' before the curtain of self-doubt descended and Jack Merridrew marched along the beach with his choristers to spoil the party; since then, nearly all of the institutions I have attended or worked in have been blighted by bullyboy Jacks and I have identified increasingly with the introverted loner Simon.

Holidays were now split between my two step-family units. My mother and stepfather Alex had moved back from India in 1964 to London where they had a flat at 90 Cornwall Gardens off Gloucester Road and spent holidays in a house they built in Andorra, whilst my father had re-married an Austrian girl called Gerlinde and moved with Burmah Oil to head up their operations in Karachi, Pakistan. My brother James was now of an age to join me in holiday visits shared between the two households. Andorra was a beautiful, still unspoilt, 'Eden' offering the delights of mountain walking and skiing, but no cricket. In the absence of cricket, I took to wafting my hands at imaginary cricket balls and bowling stones down mountains – a source of both irritation and consternation to my mother, who must have wondered about the expensive education I was being put through in Devon.

Pakistan, however, returned me to the sub-continent where I had first experienced cricket. In the mid-to-late 60s, the political scene in Pakistan was volatile and still raw from the horrors of the cataclysmic genocide inflicted during the Partition of India in 1947. While the new nation state of India moved towards embracing (despite the continuing endemic corruption) democratic principles of elected government, Pakistan oscillated between privileged Europhile democratic political dynasties like the Bhuttos and hardline extremist Muslim groups, creating a political vortex that regularly required military intervention and the imposition of martial law to restore order. As a boy on the cusp of puberty, such political awareness was not top of my priority list. Instead my father's new job came with a large company-owned mansion called White Lodge fully manned by a team of servants, a collection of one thousand budgerigars and a deer called Druscilla. Even more tantalisingly, it was positioned across the road from the Sind Club, which had been established for the recreation of British colonials during the Raj and continued to operate as if history had stopped still at 1947. Here you could while away the days playing tennis and swimming, signing chits for plates of chips and Coca Colas delivered by bearers whose heads were swathed in lavish turbans. The Sind Club also possessed a squash club which was run by the famous Khan dynasty, and I was soon mesmerised by the sight of a barefoot seven-year-old 'marker', one of the family's children, running a fit young public school stag fresh from England around the court with laughable ease. Along with cricket, squash became another ball-playing obsession with me and I would regularly cross the road on a muggy morning and request that the world number two give me a lesson.

Cricket, field hockey and squash on the sub-continent were the sports passionately pursued by the Indian and Pakistani middle-classes (the division between the nationalities was less obvious then), who had inherited the game from the British colonialists and soon started to out-perform them by displaying a more natural aptitude for games requiring such instinctive hand-eye co-ordination. The Indian genetic type (Maharashtrans, Bengalis, South Indians) tended to be smaller of stature but devastatingly quick in reactions and deft with their wrists – who can forget the sublime late cuts of 'Little Vishy' Vishwanath or the vicious spin wrought by Chandrasekhar through his polio-afflicted (and loosened!) wrist? The Pakistanis, however, usually boasted the larger Punjabi frame of the North West and could call on their Pathani warrior-tribe genes from the rugged Himalayan hinterlands to produce fast-bowling, hard-hitting all-rounders like Imran Khan. While my own games-playing was nurtured on the playing fields of England, there is no doubt that I imbibed a strong imaginative influence from these more exotic cricketers that has stayed with me throughout my extended but hardly glorious cricketing career.

During 1969 my father, as 'head honcho' at Burmah Oil, was approached to organise the tour itinerary of the forthcoming MCC Tour to Pakistan (or West Pakistan as it was known then; East Pakistan, on the far side of the Bay of Bengal, had yet to become Bangladesh). Nowadays, cricketers can fly in and out of countries to attend an IPL match here or join a tour there with seeming independent ease, but in those days cricket tours, particularly to countries like Pakistan, were like military campaigns into the unknown and you utilised any insider expertise that you could locate to smooth your path. The Test series was troubled from the outset and came unstuck in the third Test in Karachi when riots broke out and the tour had to be abandoned. Behind the scenes, my father, the MCC captain Colin Cowdrey (who grew in estimation in my father's eyes for his diplomatic perspicacity) and the belligerent President of Pakistan General Yahya Khan held emergency talks over a bottle of whisky (mostly consumed by the barrel-chested inebriate Yahya Khan) and made the final resolution to assert the restoration of public order over the continuation of the scheduled tour. As a result, my father's cricketing kudos leapt exponentially in my eyes from his previously slightly perfunctory displays of paternal co-operation in the net in Cornwall. Further reports of a garden party held at White Lodge in which Colin Milburn entertained the assembled company with his operatic baritone and Basil d'Oliveira flirted outrageously with my stepmother Gerlinde impressed me further. An additional picking included the gift of one of Cowdery's signed bats and a framed photo of the MCC tour party which hangs in my study to this day.

On my next holiday to Karachi, my father organised an opportunity for me to meet some of the Pakistan Test team, including one of my heroes the 'Little Master' Hanif Mohammad.

The occasion was the wedding reception of Asif Iqbal, the famous all-rounder who became a great servant of Kent CC. Rather embarrassingly, a year later, I was boasting of my supposed familiarity with the Pakistan Test players to Bill Cooper, my housemaster at Sherborne, who informed me that a couple of the 1971 touring party were due to come down to Sherborne to give a coaching session as part of their wider public relations campaign. Excited on my behalf, or perhaps deciding to give his scepticism about my claim an airing, he arranged for us to be introduced to Wasim Bari and another player. We duly arrived at the scene where the coaching session was taking place and, with dread filling my boots, I trumpeted to Wasim Bari: "I know you. I went to Asif Iqbal's wedding." Wasim Bari gave me a withering glare as if to say "oh yeah and who are you, punk?" and looked straight through me before resuming his coaching session. It was a good lesson in the mortification which can follow from thoughtless name-dropping!

Sherborne years

On a frosty January day in 1969 I stood with my mother at the West Hill junction looking down over the ancient sandstone town of Sherborne. We were due to attend the 'Newboys' tea party at Westcott House where I would be introduced to the housemaster tasked with the responsibility of ushering me through my adolescence. The January intake was a small one as most of my year had joined in the preceding September, and there were two other newboys, Peter Kent and Toby Wingfield-Digby who became a great friend. The housemaster, Bill Cooper, was a prematurely white-haired geography teacher who suffered from hyperhidrosis and a leg crippled through polio. He had been a prolific all-round sportsman until the handicap stopped his career at a very early age, and he was resigned to live his sport vicariously through the boys in his house. The tea party was excruciating – as these events always are – but my mother was quite taken with the charm and perfect manners of the Head of House, Toby's cousin Andrew Wingfield-Digby, a tall patrician-looking young man who exuded the nonchalant charm and sense of entitlement effused by the landed classes. She was sure that I would develop an equivalent polish through osmosis and has never quite got over the disappointment at my atrociously gauche social skills.

Sherborne was bigger, rougher, more competitive and intimidating after the comparatively gentle idyll of St Michael's. Gathered around the beautiful landmark Sherborne Abbey and the adjacent main school Courts, the school populace was domiciled in boarding houses spread across the town. Westcott House was the furthest removed from the main school buildings but closest to the Upper playing fields, which were in many ways the hub of this institution steeped in the late Victorian sporting ethic of 'mens sana in corpore sano'. The school was a notch down academically from the first-division elite of public schools such as Eton and Winchester but was the perfect breeding ground for confident all-rounders who could be moulded into exemplar institutional men and in due course take up senior positions in the city or the armed services. That said, Sherborne has also nurtured more than its fair share of misfit geniuses: the mathematics prodigy who effectively invented the computer and thus shaped the 21st century, Alan Turing, was deeply unhappy during his time at the school and was later persecuted by an unforgiving British Establishment on account of his homosexuality which they termed 'degeneracy'; he committed suicide in 1954 at the age of 41. In my time, I can remember a brilliant youth called Andrew Harvey who concealed his misery through flaunting a doomed and flamboyant 'poét maudit' persona against the backdrop of Sherborne's muddy rugby pitches – unlike Turing, who was caught in a post-war decade unable to forgive his 'degeneracy', Harvey was later able to embrace the freedoms of a world made possible by the revolution in social and sexual mores which took place during the '60s and '70s.

Newboys were given a two-week period of grace during which they were prepped by a boy immediately senior to pass an orientation test on the school's obscure customs and history. My mentor was a clever Classics scholar who already had 'future Civil Service mandarin' tattooed on his forehead, and I can recall having to undergo interminable quizzes on pieces of information such as ... the precise colour configurations on the tie awarded to the Captain of Fives or how many cats the housemaster of Lyon House possessed. These facts have stayed with me long after many a boring Chemistry lesson has slipped into the murky recesses of memory. Ask any self-tortured old public schoolboy in the throes of his mid-life crisis what colour socks you are entitled to if you win your 3rd XI hockey colours and I bet he can remember better than his wife's favourite perfume. Having passed the test, your erstwhile friendly mentor was liable to morph overnight into a sadistic tormentor. In my case, I was sent by him up to the tuck shop to buy a bag of mixed fruit contraceptives. Innocently grateful to him for having inducted me through my initiation test, I eagerly requested the afore-mentioned items. A kindly middle-aged lady smiled at me over the tuckshop counter and purred in a soft Dorset burr: "Did you mean the liquorice comfits, dear?"

From 1968 to 1973, the fagging system changed from Flashmanesque exploitation to a very watered-down round of menial housetasks, one which any mother might expect from her teenage son. When I joined Sherborne it was 1969 and the relationship between prefect and fag was every bit as homo-erotically and sado-masochistically charged as that depicted in Lindsay Anderson's seminal film 'If', an iconoclastic portrait of public school life colliding with the '60s. A prefect could summon you from the Day Room and order you to take his suit into the dry cleaners and pick up a shopping list of items whenever it pleased him; if you failed to polish his shoes to the required standard, you were given a punishment called 'Calling'. This entailed performing a striptease from suit to games clothes to Corps kit (and back again) interspersed with cold showers, once in the morning and once in the evening. Any cheek given – such as snuffling "I've got to do my Maths prep" – would lead to Double-Calling with an added return at break and after lunch for extra sessions. By 1973, however, the Sixties had swung into the decadent early Seventies. Jim Morrison, Jimi Hendrix and Janis Joplin had all died of drug overdoses and bisexual David Bowie was the trending style icon. By now toffee-nosed prefects were expected to polish their own shoes – the result of a well overdue egalitarianism sweeping the nation. In due course when I reached the 6th Form I wasn't even elected as a prefect, having long since been forsaken by any Ralph-like powers to exact respect from my subordinates (a test I put to the proof for 33 years of masochistic wage-earning in a series of classrooms across southern England!), so I never did get my chance to play Hitler with a bunch of fresh-faced newbies.

As ever, cricket was the drug of choice. Although the competition for team places had escalated, I found a place in the under-14, 15 and 16 first teams as a utility player coming in to bat at six or seven and bowling third or fourth change. Already a group of games-playing 'chaps' had formed an elite and they

Fashion car crash
Sherborne cricket blazer collides with classic 70s mullet

egged each other on through school, bagging the best roles in the teams. In the 6th Form they elected each other as prefects, bullied the younger members of staff, passed the few 'up for it girls' resident at the somewhat forbidding girls' school up the road and were licensed to smoke and drink on Saturday nights at the JCR. Years later, I remember seeing William Boyd's 'Good and Bad at Games' (remember seeing! rather, I watched it ad nauseum on the VCR with Radley students during Friday afternoon lessons) and experiencing a depressively nuanced connection to a particularly poignant moment when the protagonist 'Woggie' Niles overhears a conversation outside the Pavilion between two supposed games-playing friends busy assassinating his marginal character behind his back ... "Poor old Woggie, always sort of hanging on with that pathetic hangdog expression on his face. As if we would take a character like that seriously ... poor old Woggie, always on the outside, only put up with him because he was good for a few runs." And I thought – yes, that's how these schools work. The 'chaps' form their coteries at school and carry on through university and into the city, making sure that only the right 'chaps' get the goodies; the outsiders either compromise and catch the crumbs off the table, rebel, or bounce in and out of mental institutions. It's all cheerfully documented in 'The Making of Them: the British Attitude to Children and the Boarding School System' by Nick Duffell.

When not playing cricket for the school we played inter-house matches and when not playing house matches we played cricket with a tennis ball in the back yard. Bill Cooper was so keen to keep us hitting balls that he even blocked out a series of friendly house matches against local village teams on Sunday afternoons. One afternoon we were mini-bussed off to a ground in deepest rural Dorset and bowled out for the princely total of three runs! Bill arrived at 2.20 in his car to find us all milling about the pavilion. "Have you tossed up yet?" he asked anxiously. "No, sir, the game's over, we were all out for 3." "Oh, who scored the runs?" "Floyer snicked the first ball through the slips, sir." "Oh ..." A beer match was hastily arranged to take us up to the tea lavishly prepared by the village's cricket ladies.

From the moment I arrived at Sherborne I was drawn to the Upper where the 1st XI played its school matches. Until the UK exam system became chronically persistent, convoluted and time consuming, the summer term stretched from the middle of April to late July, and 1st XI games were often played over a leisurely two days with both sides getting two innings (like a Test match). I would dash down to the ground at every available opportunity to see my heroes – Phil Lough, the opener, and all-rounder Ed Fursdon – grace the hallowed turf. I promised myself that if I failed at every other aspect of school life I would at least one day feel the golden thwack of bat on ball in a Sherborne cricket shirt. A key figure on the school staff was the diminutive figure of Micky Walford, one of the great Corinthian sportsmen of the amateur age, who had played rugby and hockey for England and turned out for Somerset CCC in the school holidays. A bachelor housemaster of Abbey House, he taught Economics (well, kind of) but his real value lay in his wonderful one-on-one coaching skills. There was nothing that he didn't understand about the deft and subtle interplay between bat/stick/racquet and human wrist to facilitate the propulsion of a ball into the precise space intended. If you were any sort of ball player at all he would make it his mission to give you his undivided attention for as long as it took to get you playing the right shot. What a privilege it was to have this sporting god taking a personal interest in developing your very limited skills from behind the net as you carried out his instructions to "keep your head still as you meet the ball".

Joining the sixth form was a breath of fresh air after the cleated-down existence of the lower school. I was free to specialise in my favourite subjects, English and History, and spent hours consuming and virtually living in the world of the 19th century Russian novelists Tolstoy, Turgenev and Dostoyevsky. In fact, as I recall this febrile stage of my intellectual and emotional growth, I can feel myself shivering on the Russian steppes and dreaming of the shadowy interiors of Moscow salons where I might meet the Natasha Rostov of my dreams. Unlike today's child-centred nanny-state sixth forms where teachers frantically spoon-feed helpless and needy sixth formers with the necessary information to keep the school's percentage of A and A* grades up to scratch, the sixth form at Sherborne provided a student with a staff of scholarly but essentially distant teachers, labyrinthine library shelves stocked with erudite tomes within which you were expected to get lost as you researched weekly essays, and lots of societies to which you were invited if you displayed the right mettle. Sherborne was unashamedly elitist in its assumption that by the age of sixteen a young person should be able to marshall his or her resources of time and energy independently. At some stage during the two-year course one either found oneself placed on the Oxbridge conveyor belt or plotting to escape academia and head for a jackaroo station in Queensland: 'chaps' could either hack the academic world or were urged towards a life of gentlemanly adventure 'roughing it' in England's ex-colonies.

Sex was another pre-occupation. Semen-stained porn mags circulated the warren of studies in Westcott House where testosterone-crazed adolescents were housed in feral proximity to one another. The innocent homophilia of prep school had given way to a frustrated and aggressive heterosexuality that released itself in buckets of sperm ejaculated and sluiced down the communal toilets. The bolder spirits amongst us boasted girlfriends either from home or resident at the neighbouring girl schools and talked about parties in the holidays where they claimed to 'get the whole way'. The alternative for the chronically shy was to read about the hedonistic exploits of the Beat poets, the novels of Henry Miller and DH Lawrence's high-minded but determinedly sexual liminal states of dark electric forces between loins and swooning states of polarised sex oneness (yes, it was that garbled). If lucky, you might be able to attend a Scottish dancing event at the girls' school and encounter an equally tortured member of the opposite sex and dance the Gay Gordons, sweaty hands clasped around damp waists in a gathering fug of pheromones, furtive urine secretions and stilted conversation whilst resident staff looked on benignly from the sidelines and sipped schooners of sherry.

Home life had moved on, too. The arrival of an au pair into my mother's household, a gorgeous teenage Spanish girl called Patricia (pronounced 'Patreetsia' with an Andalus flourish of plosives) brought a frisson of romance into my pimply self-conscious adolescence. She was the daughter of an old friend of my stepfather and hailed from ancient Spanish aristocratic stock. A sultry beauty with a fine aquiline nose which seemed to quiver at each new impression, Patricia was nevertheless delightfully down to earth, and I fell blushingly into a kind of teen love-crush. With disregard for my speechless moon-eyed adoration of her, she made it clear that she was betrothed to a boyfriend who was in the sixth form at Eastbourne – and that was that. A few years later she was briefly married to a Sicilian Count whose father had been a notorious old goat who would summon the bells in his palazzio to be rung every time he made love to one of his young mistresses. When the marriage failed, Patricia went back to Spain and helped her mother run a boutique in Marbella – strange how some lives seem to drift to the margins.

My brother James had joined me at Sherborne. Six and a half years younger than me, he was placed at the prep school just over the wall from Westcott House. On weekends I would eke him out from those wafting boarding school smells of carbolic soap, airfix glue and dusty Latin primers and we'd wander around the environs of Sherborne town speaking into a cassette recorder about the weekly dramas of our cloistered lives; I would then send the tape off home in lieu of a letter. The prep school was run by the notorious paedophile Robin Lindsay who managed to escape detection, retire and die before the full scale of his crimes became public knowledge. I remember how we used to watch from the balconies of Westcott House as he assembled the whole school into North Korean parade-ground-style formations on the playing field. He'd then instruct a hundred young boys to "lift" their bats, "front foot forward" and "play". Whilst his charges duly obeyed his instructions he would sniff around their techniques, correcting a skewed wrist here or a misplaced trouser leg there. We all thought he was grooming the next generation of Geoffrey Boycotts when in fact he was lining up his talent on a perverse 'catwalk' so that he could select the choice morsels for his nefarious attentions. Luckily my brother's forward defensive was never classically orthodox enough to catch his eye.

My father, meanwhile, had moved from Pakistan to Sydney, Australia. He was at the peak of his powers as an executive with Burmah Oil and was housed in a gorgeous company house in Balgowlah Heights with views across the magnificent middle harbour. On alternate holidays, my brother and I were flown out from school to Sydney where we exchanged a bleak strike-bound early 70s UK for the sunlight and outdoor life of our

Ashes rivals. Days were spent lounging in a boat named 'Gotcha' and trawling the many beaches which front the harbour, or in my case taking the Manly Ferry to the CBD and heading over to watch Dougie Walters hooking the ball into the stands from the famous Sydney CC Hill. Closer to home, my stepmother Gerlinde employed the services of a beautiful blonde neighbour to baby-sit her young daughter (my half-sister Ceal, later to become a successful conceptual artist) when my parents went out to evening social events. Although I was nearly eighteen Gerlinde quite rightly didn't trust me to look after the household by myself, so this blonde bombshell would arrive, put Ceal to bed and then cook me a dinner of sausages and chips. Although blushing, stammering and tongue-tied, I thought my tales of English public school life might perhaps intrigue her sufficiently into some sort of relationship. I was soon put right (or 'put roight') by the arrival of Brad, a hunky Neanderthal surfer who checked me over, trailed a spoor of butch Aussie male essence through the house to keep his Sheila in tow and then left to sink a few 'tinnies' with his mates. Talk about being well and truly baby-sat!

It was not until the Easter holiday before my last term at school that my luck turned. By now, my mother and stepfather Alex had moved full-time to Torremolinos in southern Spain where they had built a hotel (the first stage of a complex of hotels: Don Pedro, Don Pablo and Don Marco) by the beachfront on the Paseo Maritimo. The early '70s had witnessed an explosion of cheap charter flight holidays to the Spanish Costas, and Torremolinos, which had until only recently been a sleepy fishing village favoured by bohemian drifters, was now the Magaluf of the day, notorious for attracting lager-swilling Germans and pasty-skinned Northerners on the pull for birds and booze. A friend of the family Gervais, a rather gauche ex-Downside boy from a Catholic family, had driven down from Andorra to stay with us and see if he could join the party. It was a commonly held maxim that if a bloke couldn't get laid in Torremolinos, he might as well embrace celibacy for life. Every night Gervais and

I embarked on quixotic nocturnal jaunts through the 'free for all' bar and nightclub zones of Combat Alley looking for 'action'; night after night, two losers staggered back to the hotel in a fug of slurred despair. However, one evening as we traipsed into the hotel lobby at 3 a.m., we were pounced on by two lipstick-smudged lasses from Bolton. Over the previous days we had been watching these girls around the hotel and making derisive comparisons to the svelte Swedish sirens we were convinced lay in store for us. Grabbing me by the belt of my bellbottoms, one of them called Karen said: "Eh you, you'se stopping with 'oos tonight. Coom 'ere." Terrified out of our wits but sufficiently pissed on San Miguel to go along with our first and only carnal opportunity, we bundled into their shared hotel room. A little while later we were bundled out of the room red-faced with horror and still just about penis intactus.

Summer term 1973 – my last school cricket season. I bowled, batted and fielded my heart out during the early season nets training in the hope of securing a starting slot in the XI: there were seven pencilled in as certainties and another four berths between about eight of us. The captain John Garforth-Bles had been a star batsman in the XI for four years but he wasn't a mate of mine, so I knew that I had to put in more than 100% to catch the eye. As a hockey player I could count on Micky Walford's support; nevertheless, I was hugely excited and relieved when I saw my name up on the team sheet for the opening match on the noticeboard in the Cloisters. There I was – ninth on the list – selected to represent the Sherborne 1st XI against the Dorset Rangers as a second string all-rounder. This was undoubtedly the highlight so far in my burgeoning career as a cricket tragic.

It was a damp Saturday in May, and we were put into bat on a wicket which skidded and bounced irregularly as it so often does in an early-season match. Wickets tumbled steadily throughout the pre-lunch session, and I went through the tortured rigamarole of emotions that precedes a march to the crease from the pavilion: apprehensive euphoria at being there at all as I strapped on my pads, followed by a hope that coming in at number seven I would just be required to add a little cameo after the big guns up the order had filled their boots, and deep down a furtive demon that wished ill on all of the front-line batsmen so that my failure might be overshadowed by theirs, succeeded by a fantasy that I would come out from the late middle order and heroically save the side. Round and round these thoughts churned until the fifth wicket fell just before lunch and I was marching out to the crease with the side in deep trouble.

After lunch I resumed my innings. The Dorset Rangers captain – 'Wog' Hunter, a Physics teacher so named because of his shock of frizzy hair (we were all unashamedly unreconstructed racists in those days) who coached the 1st XI side – was clearly keen to manufacture a match, so he brought himself on to bowl and fed me a series of rank half-trackers outside off stump which I dabbed through gully and point. It was an act of charity on his part, but I was in no mood to look his calculated gifthorse in the mouth and, much to my amazement, I found myself eight runs short of a fifty when I holed out for 42. My first match for the XI and I was top scorer – life has rarely approached such dizzy heights of joy since that moment. Later when we tried to defend our total in the field I was tossed the ball by the captain and told that it was my day. I snaffled two wickets in my first over and, by the time the Rangers had overhauled our modest score, I had the best bowling analysis, too. What was that other great all-rounder Ian Botham doing on that day? By my calculation he would have been six months younger than me; I bet he didn't get 42 runs and two wickets ... well, maybe he did.

I describe this match with indulgent loving detail because – as I realise forty or so years later – my cricket career never again scaled such heights. And the 42 is published in Wisden 1974. Oh the frisson of joy which still accompanies an old cricketing codger's reminiscent fingering of the well-thumbed page in his treasured copy!

The season plateaued for the next two games. I scored a twenty in the first game and in the second added a supportive 24 to a partnership at Clifton College (yes, the home of Henry

Newbolt's famous line 'Play up! Play! And play the game!') with a six-foot-seven beanstalk called Hugh Leman, who smashed a brilliant match-winning 70-odd runs coming in at number nine. However, the tide was subtly turning and some eye-catching performances by my rivals in the 2nd XI were undermining my right to a place in the team. Next match I was out for a duck against Westminster on Vincent's Square (I have never scored a run in the capital, my birthplace) and then foolishly swished rankly across the line against Canford for another zero. My chips were up, and my mood dipped. Like a sulky Achilles, I withdrew to my study and wallowed in Crosby, Stills, Nash and Young's recently released album 'Déjà vu', wailing: "Helpless helpless helpless ... heeeellllplus." It was still only mid-June and the pitches were hardening up, yet my season seemed to be over. It was just as well probably. I had the small matter of 'A' levels to distract me from the more important demise of my batting form.

The last month of the term went by in a blur. With a couple of friends, I helped to organise a 48-hour non-stop charity cricket match to raise money for Cancer Research and this parallel commitment dominated my time. At some point in the exam room I encountered Ted Hughes' poem 'Thrushes' and discovered another activity which almost approaches cricket for sheer consciousness-consuming joy: close practical poetry criticism (thanks Ted, you got me to Oxford). I was briefly re-instated in the 1st XI for the match against the MCC and thrashed their fast bowler off the back foot through the covers in a gesture of doomed bravado (a shot I still re-play in my head), and very generously the school awarded me my cricket colours because I had accumulated the 100 runs needed to be included in the Schools averages section in Wisden. This entitled me to purchase the startling turquoise-and-gold tie over which I had been covetously salivating ever since my newboys test five years earlier and to rim my turquoise cricket blazer with gold braid. I was trussed like a peacock and ready to strut out to the crease of Life and make my school proud ... hoho ...

Oxford

A talent for creating subversive and surreal subtext narratives for the war comic 'trash mags' which circulated the studies in House (and gave me the confidence to follow through the most outrageous speculations about unseen poems in the Practical Criticism paper), an obsessive interest in 19th century Russian literature and a recent discovery of Blake and Lawrence underpinned the huge fluke of winning a scholarship to read English Literature at Wadham College. At Sherborne, although I had been edged into the Oxbridge conveyor belt, it was assumed that it was most likely the possibility of my gaining a hockey blue which would be the clincher rather than any innate intellectual prowess. As Bill Cooper never tired of telling me: "You're a dark horse, Floyer."

The choice of Wadham was prompted by the Floyer family's Founder's Kin connection to the original founders of the College, Nicholas and Dorothy Wadham (generally referred to as Nick and Dot), rather than an ambition to study under the Oxford's most 'right on' tutor, Terry Eagleton, the brilliant and controversial Marxist critic who was the 'bête noir' of the Oxford English faculty. So, the city of dreaming spires and perspiring dreams beckoned.

Meantime I had nine months to put in before I could go 'up' to Oxford. Although my father was delighted at this unexpected academic success, he was worried that I would now turn into a rarefied 'namby pamby' aesthete straight out of 'Brideshead Revisited' and determined that I should put the fallow time to use by growing hair on my chest (metaphorically speaking). So, no gap year trips to gorge on the Renaissance masters in the Uffizi in Florence or preliminary familiarisation with the Anglo-Saxon texts which would greet me at Oxford. Instead, he arranged to have me posted to a cattle ranch in Northern Queensland with the expectation that I should come back with a square jaw, a wild thirst for 'stubbies' of lager and a rough-and-ready Aussie drawl.

This is not the time to go into detail about the three-month debacle which ensued. Suffice to say, I failed to chisel my jawline during my two-week spell as a jackaroo, took flight with my rucksack on my back and waded through the extreme floods which hit Northern Queensland that January before embarking on a lonely descent of the Eastern Australian seaboard, kipping in squalid flop-houses and living off meat pies – very 'Midnight Cowboy'! Eventually my savings ran out, and I determined to use the last of my funds to hitch-hike around Tasmania just so that I could return to England equipped with one positive story. Landing at Heathrow six months before intended, I still had time to put in before Oxford, so I stayed with the Glens in Hampstead and found a retail job at Foyle's bookshop on the Charing Cross Road.

The English cricket season was just beginning with the first-class fixture list opening at Fenner's and the Parks in semi-arctic conditions. For the first time in ten years, spring beckoned without any early season nets or fixture list of matches to look forward to. I was still reeling from Australia and had developed an unhealthy obsession with Bruce Lee's cinematic kung-fu acrobatics, on top of the continuing crush I had on Mia Farrow as I fantasised about rescuing her from the coven of creepy New York Satanists in 'Rosemary's Baby'. I probably needed a therapist! Instead, I spent most of my spare time tootling down St John's Wood Road to Lord's to watch Middlesex begin the toil of a long county season.

In the days before back-to-back 20-over thrashes accompanied by endless hype aimed at fans with ADD attention spans, watching cricket was very 'zen'. You would prepare a little rucksack with some sandwiches, a packet of Walkers crisps, an apple, a KitKat and a flask of tea. Then you'd tuck in a scorebook (if seriously tragic) or at least a Playfair cricket annual to provide thumbnail biographies of the players – very important to reflect on the fact that the batsman you've been watching for the last two hours of play, MJ Harris of Notts and Middx, has a nickname of 'Pasty' and was born on 25 May 1944 at St Just-in-Roseland. On the way into the ground you might pick up a newspaper – another subtle pleasure: glancing between the news stories of the day and a lazily executed late cut out on the square, feeling both in the world and detached from it (I'm sure politicians would make many more sensible decisions if they watched more cricket – I guess we should look at the career of John Major to prove the efficacy, or otherwise, of this observation!). On entering the ground you'd draw in a deep breath – ah! Lord's! – before perambulating a clockwise circuit of the ground to find the optimal seat: in my case, a forty-five degree angle on play from the elevation of ten tiers of seats, preferably with the sun shining across my face on a slant. With luck, the spectators might total under a hundred and include an Irish playwright escaping from Parisian existential life to nurse a covert passion for cricket (is that rather intense figure with spectacles and a hawk nose sitting three rows down really Samuel Beckett? or just another cricket-mad prep school French teacher dodging class?). At 10.55 a.m. a bell rings and two white-coated umpires make their way out to the square, followed by eleven fielders (in those days probably finishing off a fag; nowadays vigorously swinging limbs accompanied by a team of physios) and two batsmen in peaked caps. What ensued would usually be a leisurely contest between bat and ball at about two runs per over (nowadays batsmen clutch their heads in despair if they haven't swished the ball for at least a two). Occasionally the ball might thud into the boundary board followed by a faint quiver of uplifted faces in the crowd and some muted applause. Lunch at 1.00 usually involved a watery pint of John Smith's from Father Time's Bar, followed by a stroll around the ground in an anti-clockwise direction. You'd possibly catch a glimpse of one of the players having a crafty fag on the player's balcony before play resumed, and in this way the day would unfold with somnolent ease. Around the world, stock market traders shriek at the Dow Jones, some coup is taking place in central Africa, the banks of the Ganges have burst, but you could nod gently through the afternoon at two runs per over till stumps were drawn at 6.00 p.m.

I saw many splendid sights that summer. The blonde dasher Clive Radley never failed to entertain whilst the evergreen (and toe-less) off-spinner Freddie Titmus continued to wheel in and ply his trade. I fulfilled an ambition to see the great Gary Sobers bat when he stroked an effortless 74 in Nottinghamshire colours, barely breaking into a canter. I was there when the two seaming shire-horses Chris Old and Geoff Arnold bowled India out for 42 in an hour – a flurry of activity which included two sixes from the Indian all-rounder Eknath Solkar. I was there, I was there, I was there ... and never once did I feel guilty that I really ought to have been elsewhere.

By October 1974 I was due to start my Oxford life. The scholarship I'd won swiftly seemed fraudulent as we first-year Freshers gathered in the Wadham Dining Hall for the first formal evening meal and I glimpsed rows of 'boffinous'-looking individuals in their gowns sparking up frantically self-conscious polysyllabic conversations about the meaning of life to show how clever they were. Wadham had historically been a relatively obscure college compared to the big powerhouses such as Christchurch, Merton, New and Balliol colleges. It boasted some famous alumni – most notably Sir Christopher Wren and the famous Oxford figure Sir Maurice Bowra – but retained the spirit of its modest original charter to educate the sons of West Country gentry. The arrival of the 1960s, however, brought out the college's innate liberal leanings as it courted a wider social mix of entrants and became a focal point for left-wing student activity. By the time I went up, it had developed a 'cool' image as being less stuffy and public-school-orientated than most colleges. 1974 was also the first year in which women were admitted as an experiment into all-male colleges and Wadham was one of the five pioneers to accept them (seems rather quaint now).

The English tutorials were run in tandem by Terry Eagleton and the Anglo-Saxon expert Alan Ward. Terry was still only in his early thirties when I joined his tutorial group but had already carved out a considerable reputation as a brilliant and iconoclastic literary critic. Ostracised by the more traditional bastion of Oxford 'letters', he was determined to bring the work of the continental post-structuralist and Marxist-historicist intellectuals to bear upon the university's cultural life. After the first tutorial, our group of eight (seven male, one female) were set an essay on a Marxist-Historicist reading of the Brontë sisters to be handed in one week later. This was all very well but I hadn't even read 'Jane Eyre' and 'Wuthering Heights' yet, let alone digested the works of Lacan, Raymond Williams, Derrida and Foucault. The pressure was on. Luckily Alan, our tutor for the Old English first-year requirement, was a delightfully shy and sympathetic old-style academic who would cough and wheeze through his tutorials, giving contorted imitations of the early vowel stutterings of Palaeolithic man and thankfully misplacing (or losing) all the essays one gave him on Aelfric and other pre-Chaucerian entertainments. Every now and then, it would all get too much for him and he would hastily excuse himself from the room. Only later did we learn that Alan was an avid gambler and student of the turf and that his interruptions provided a necessary exit to place a last minute bet on the 2.30 at Wincanton.

Oxford terms are only eight weeks long so you need to hit the road running if you want to achieve your aims. My only aim was survival, which wasn't helped by the female member of our tutorial group casting me in the role of Lenny in Pinter's 'The Dwarfs' for the inter-collegiate 'Cuppers' drama competition. Lenny's inpenetrable introverted monologues proved almost impossible for me to learn, and I fear that my performance did little to kickstart her dramatic credentials at Oxford, not that it held her back from a diverse later career as a musician, actress and director. I also made the mistake, after watching Johan Cruyff and his magnificent orange shirts redefine football with their total football game in the 1974 World Cup, of thinking that I would like to resume my footballing career. I hadn't touched a football since prep school and foolishly threw myself into an ill-judged tackle in my first game for the college 2nd XI, badly injuring the tendons around my right knee. This effectively discounted me from trialling for the hockey blues squad (a long shot anyway), and I hobbled around Oxford throughout the damp winter months feeling quite sorry for myself.

The relationship between Oxford and undergraduate misery is well charted. I'm not surprised that it has led to off-the-scale suicide rates amongst its demographic sample. Check out the recipe: you place a sensitive and often socially gauche young person in a hothouse of academic (and related) achievement; you speed the clock up so that everything is expected to be done brilliantly yesterday; you surround him or her with examples of stellar achievement executed with seemingly nonchalant ease. Failure isn't really an option. Is it any surprise that every year a percentage of undergraduates feel trapped into taking the only exit which seems possible? Looking back at my first year at Oxford, I realise that I was in the throes of a state of permanent low-level depression. Most of my days were spent alone tussling with an escalating treadmill of reading and essay assignments; come the evening, I felt too edgy to relax and join the social whirl which always seemed to be happening just out of my reach. There is no more beautiful and lonely place than the Radcliffe Camera lit up on a frosty winter's night as you take a final solitary stroll at 10.00 p.m. on a Saturday evening to purchase a kebab from the 'Deathburger' van parked on the High and catch the blasts of student laughter and music drifting over from an adjacent college quad: all the gilded youth are in the throes of revelry and your soul feels as shrivelled as that of an ascetic 13th century monk. Still, at least I kept out of the Warneford mental hospital in Headington where one of us 'eaglets' ended up ...

... and then I fell in love with a dead female English novelist! She stared balefully out at me from the frames of photos taken by her Bloomsbury circle of family and friends. She wrote poetically about rarefied sensitives on the verge of nervous collapse quivering through their stream of consciousness internal monologues. Yes, she seemed to say to me, we are both too delicate for the rude intercourse of this world, we must retreat to our inner selves and net the waves of thought breaking bleakly on the shoreline of our subconscious. How much easier it was to commune with her in a carrel in the Bodleian or wander through the Parks with a copy of 'Mrs Dalloway' tucked under my sweater than to have to talk to a real-live girl in the flesh.

Yes, it was definitely time for Cricket to come to the rescue! Oxford in the spring is one of the most intoxicating places on earth. The rainclouds lift from the Thames valley, and the medieval college buildings are bathed in amber sunshine. Blonde-haired bluestockings with names like Ariadne shake their tresses over their black gowns as they cycle from St Hilda's into the libraries to swot all day for the looming examinations. A febrile energy grips the town as the twin rivers of high-minded intellectual aspiration and carefree hedonism collide and mingle. There's no better place to graze with your books than The Parks on a sunny morning where the university team might be playing a visiting county side in a warm-up match. Then to cycle off to the Wadham ground for an afternoon of cricket followed by draughts of Moreland's ale in the pavilion. Idyllic.

Wadham's cricket side reflected the broad liberal ethos and social make-up of the college. For the first time in my life, I played cricket in a truly recreational spirit. It didn't really matter if you scored a fifty or were out for a duck. Dress code was informal – two of our cover point fielders were hippies who smoked dope on the boundary and fielded barefoot with their long locks swept back in a bandana. I can remember the motley crew of Wadhamite cricketers turning up for a Cuppers first-round game against snooty St John's and being bowled out by the future England spinner Vic Marks for a one-digit total. "Nice one, mate," we looked up at him and grinned as another one of his fizzing off-breaks darted through our ill-prepared defences to clatter into the stumps. CB Fry, Wadham's most distinguished alumni cricketer and all-round sportsman, would have turned in his grave ... or maybe not – he was notoriously eccentric, being reputedly offered the throne of Albania, possessing the ability to jump backwards on to a mantelpiece as a party trick and once being arrested wandering around naked in Brighton. In these laid-back conditions I thrived and was encouraged to bat at whatever position I chose and to bowl all afternoon, and my season ended with a glorious knock of 99 for Wadham South against Wadham North followed by the customary piss-up in

Wadham College XI – Summer of '76

the pavilion and, for once, there was no cerebral-looking Virginia Woolf hovering on the boundary's edge.

When I look back at my time at Oxford I wish I had been just a little bolder and more mature to take advantage of being there. After my somewhat traumatic first year in which I gained a second at Mods, I retreated into my comfort zone for the next two years: lots of sport, private reading and a pleasant but unadventurous social life. I trialled for the Oxford Hockey Blues and was invited to join the Oxford Occasionals Club (a kind of 2nd XI club like its cricketing equivalent, the Authentics) and I was selected to play for a scratch West Country side against the touring South African Under-21 side (a game in which I failed to even touch the ball as my opposite number ran circles around me). I took up karate and gymnastics and indulged in marathon sporting 'quadrathlons' with a fellow Wadham contemporary called Myron Rybcak: this would typically involve a five-mile run, followed by 100 lengths at the Summertown baths, a weights session and an hour of squash washed down with several jars of ale at the King's Arms. Academically, I lost contact with Terry Eagleton (and vice versa), but I chose to follow his advice not to attend any lectures, which I regret in hindsight, and effectively became an autodidact reading the whole canon of English and American literature on my own. Alan Ward kept an avuncular eye on me, as he did with every Wadham English student abandoned by Terry, whilst I drifted through a rota of books, sports and beer towards an unremarkable second-class degree.

Near the end of my second year I kept receiving cryptic messages from some third years that I barely knew. I was 'knowingly' tipped off that "Marlon will be back in Oxford from the States in a couple of weeks" and "Marlon was wondering if you have a girlfriend" and "Marlon was hoping you would be around to have dinner with him." I didn't know Marlon at all, though I did remember an open-faced blonde American law postgrad who tried to engage me in conversation at dinner in Hall sometime in the first year. This interest in me should have struck me as odd, but I was innocently narcissistic to the core and the prospect of anyone treating me to dinner, male or female, was intriguing. I duly met Marlon at a pub in Little Clarendon Street on a balmy late June afternoon, and we progressed to dinner at Brown's restaurant. As the evening progressed through copious amounts of alcohol and flattery, Marlon's conversation moved from innocuous chatter to more sexually suggestive and ambiguous topics. When he picked up the bill, he suggested that we should go and relax in a friend's room in Balliol. The friend, he said, had conveniently vacated his room so that we could be more private. By this stage, a nauseous realisation was belatedly dawning on me ... yes, I had obviously been carefully groomed over a whole year for this homosexual encounter. I panicked and blurted out that I was "not that way inclined, as it were" and scampered off into the backstreets of North Oxford. Marlon took the next flight back to the States, and I heard nothing about him until one day a request to 'connect' on LinkedIn came from a very successful and prominent Californian corporate advocate with an open face and a bald pate. However, I had learnt some sort of lesson and from that day on I thought carefully about poncing around Oxford in my turquoise peacock Sherborne cricket blazer ... it was clearly sending out the wrong signals.

Third year came around all too quickly and the glittering youths who had spent two years politicking in the Oxford Union and falling in and out of bed with each other whilst I mooched about searching for Virginia knuckled down to work and the 'serious' business of choosing a career. Every year the Milk Train landed in Oxford and dangled enticing management traineeships with the BBC or IBM in front of ambitious undergraduates with confident social skills, whilst the future mandarins lined up for the Civil Service exams to book a berth as a Junior Secretary in Her Majesty's embassy in Shanghai. Only now did I realise how much ground I had lost already ... a modest academic record, a private obsession or two and many hours spent cricketing with a bunch of hippies: I was hardly the polished young diamond that the competitive world of employment was looking to snaffle up. After spending many fruitless hours traipsing up to the careers office on Woodstock Road, filling in application forms only to receive the inevitable "Dear Sir, thank you for your application to become a management trainee at Kodak but ...", I decided to make an audit of what I really liked doing and go from there.

So, what was 'my bag'? I loved reading and was particularly drawn to 20th century North American writing at the time; I loved sport and was well on my way to becoming a chronic cricket tragic; I loved to write although I wasn't sure what I wanted to do with this itch (my latest piece – a pastiche of Ernest Hemingway which I submitted to the College Essay Society – had been returned to me by the President, poet Hilary Davies, between finger and thumb like an embarrassing piece of soiled underwear). I was hardly in the minority in being undecided as to how to proceed, but I'm grateful that I didn't get snarled up with a trainee-management placement at Kodak, an early mid-life crisis and a belated realisation at the age of forty that by preference I liked reading, cricket and writing. However, the options – once I had discounted the 'lonely garret' as a career path – narrowed down to teaching, teaching ... or teaching. Naturally I had no desire to teach at all, having only recently inched free from the cleats of my own schoolmasters, but I could see how a quiet life in a sleepy country public school might allow me to continue to read, play cricket and maybe write in the company of young minds with whom I would share these activities. How idealistic I was (and lazy ...), so I signed myself in for a year's PGCE at the London Institute of Education, a move, I figured, which would keep the fast-approaching world of work at bay for at least a year.

Finals is as gruelling an event as any I can think of. The Marathon des Sables, in which runners cover the equivalent of six back-to-back marathons over six days in the gruelling Sahara heat, can't be any worse. Ten three-hour papers spread over five days held in the Oxford Schools building, lined up in tiers in a kind of 'corrida' of fellow examinees, wearing a uniform of subfusc gown, scratchy bow-tie and sweat starched shirt, is not for wimps. Add to that the sheer physicality of scraping a pen frantically over an exam booklet and the requirement that three years of desultory reading in English Literature from Chaucer to the modern day needs to be committed to memory. No coursework or electronic memory gizmos to prop up your performance. Most students conduct a monastic 'hairshirt' pre-Finals routine of preparation in which every minute of the day is accounted for over a period of at least three months. However, the joy when you finally emerge from your last paper blinking at the sunlight in the High Street to be greeted by your mates opening bottles of bubbly makes it all worthwhile (well ... not really ...).

The last couple of weeks after Finals before 'I went down' were redolent with valedictory moments as my brief time at Oxford was bathed in a liquor of nostalgia for a place of aching beauty in which I had been privileged to spend an intense period of my youth. My cousin Fra was in her first year as a history undergraduate at Somerville, and we used to meet at the Cherwell boathouse and take a punt up river to the Vicki Arms and back. The conversations we had against a backdrop of colleges and fields glimpsed through leafy foliage as we trailed a gentle wake from the punt were spliced with both the optimism of new beginnings and an elegiac mood of imminent departure (Oh, how Rupert Brooke! 'Ah God! To see the branches stir/ Across the moon at Grantchester.')

It was time to move on ... I would be back in Oxford one day.

Swerving East

At some point during the summer vacation whilst awaiting my Finals result, I picked up a paperback with a lurid front cover depicting a mural of 'The Day of the Dead' by the Mexican artist Diego Rivera. In those days, grey-spined Penguins were synonymous with a 'cool intellectual' label, and this tome felt satisfyingly meaty as well as exotic. The back cover gave a synopsis of the novel's depiction of the last tragic day of Geoffrey Firmin, the alcoholic British Consul to Quahnahuac in Mexico, who drinks himself to death on the Day of the Dead 1939. Intrigued, I was playing a kind of Russian roulette: I need a book to read – this one, this one or this one, what the hell (no pun intended, Lowryans). On impulse I bought it and started to read. I had never heard of the author Malcolm Lowry and wondered why his exalted prose style and gripping themes had not found their way on to the Oxford canon. I was also secretly pleased that he seemed to be unknown as it felt, as it does whenever you pick up a great novel, as if he was speaking to me alone. A seed was planted, and over the next three years I picked up everything I could on this great British novelist and wilful obscurantist, who seemed to have slipped through the academic net. Three years later I started an M.Phil on Lowry's work and suffered the agonies of writing an extended love letter to a dead writer through the medium of a post-graduate thesis.

Meantime I was booked into my PGCE course in London and was intent, as an outrageously spoilt member of the Boomer generation, on making sure that my generous fourth-year grant was spent on having fun. Even I knew that the no-strings-attached provision of ultra-cheap accommodation in central London with pocket money provided by the taxman was a 'no brainer', especially as the early pre-teaching practice part of the course was a doddle compared to the rigours of Finals. So for two delicious months of freedom I lived like an unfettered bird with London spread before my feet. And then ... one fateful evening ... I met my future wife, and Life embarked on a heady rollercoaster of romantic 'sturm und drang'. Snezana, or Snezzy as she is known, is Serbian by origin and has quite rightly remained resolutely indifferent to my passion for cricket throughout our marriage. Maiden overs, fine legs, deep gullies and silly mid off all remain double dutch (or scrambled serb) terms to her, though she can produce a killer cricket tea when the occasion demands.

My teaching practice sent me out east to a comprehensive school in Harold Hill, just beyond Romford and literally on the edge of an estate bordering the first stretch of rural Essex. This took up four days of my week and then it was back to the weekly 'bop' at the Institute where Snezzy and I jumped around to the rousing anthems of the Stranglers' 'No More Heroes' and Bob Marley's 'Jammin'' before luxuriating through a long weekend in the capital. London was flush with Mohican-topped punks sneering and snarling through their safety pins and it seemed a tad bizarre that I should simultaneously be applying for jobs in remote private schools where chapel bells rang and teacups clinked demurely on saucers.

My first interview was at Tonbridge where a kindly but razor-sharp and bespectacled Head of English (Jonathan Smith, father of selector Ed) gently advised me that a CV needed to include a little more information than a list of cricket teams I had played for. He palmed me off on his deputy, Michael Mavor, who took me for a relaxing beer before depositing me at the headmaster's study for interview. A polite letter of rejection followed a few days later, and I set to work on my CV to become better prepared for the next interview. In due course I was offered jobs by both Framlingham in Suffolk and Felsted in Essex. I was advised that perhaps the post at Felsted was a better school to 'cut my teeth on' as a teacher new to the profession; it was also closer to London where Snezzy had secured a post in a rough comprehensive in Dagenham. So eastwards we were based over the next two years.

In 1978 Felsted was a solidly traditional and 'gamesy' public school in the heartlands of the Essex countryside. After London and Oxford, it felt very parochial and conservative – as a young single master it was considered risqué and potentially scandalous that I might be attached to a woman out of wedlock. How to account for the occasional late nocturnal visit of a young lady with long dark hair to my bachelor quarters? After about a month the deputy headmaster sidled up to me in Common Room and invited me for a chat in his study. Oh no! were the Lower Fourth that noisy? "My dear man, Floyer, are your ears not burning?" After several nods and hurrumphs, it transpired that the cause for concern was indeed the siting of a mysterious person of the female persuasion talking to me outside the Swan Inn at the scandalously late hour of 10.30 p.m.!

However, it was a great place to start my teaching career as the school's sixth form had recently become co-educational. There was an encouraging welcome extended to a young English teacher who was excited about sharing his passion for English literature with young men and women only five years younger than him and in need of tolerance for committing the odd howler of a lesson. Most of the pupils in the school came from Essex farming and professional families, and there was a distinctive bucolic look of rosy cheeks and flaxen hair. The head of department, Mike Craven, was a genuinely supportive, intelligent and laid-back character who gave me just the right amount of autonomy in the classroom before making useful interventions of guidance and advice.

Forgive me if I indulge a senior moment in my role as a curmudgeonly, recently retired classroom practitioner but a word here about how the classroom has changed from 1978 to the present day. Back then, before a lesson, students would generally line up politely to be invited into the classroom and then await your instructions as to how you wished to teach them. If you decided that they should quietly read a short story before a shared discussion they would do so with a minimum of fuss, and if you asked them to write up notes on the story for prep they would do so without throwing a wobbly and demanding that their parents hire a private tutor to help them organise their homework. By the time I left the classroom in December 2013, students would customarily jostle their way into the classroom with headphones glued to their ears. Lessons had to be carefully planned to move from activity to activity to keep the students from jumping out of their seats. If you set a prep they took a mobile phone photo of your instructions on the board and expected you to e-mail them with sheets of advice so that their tutors could write their coursework for them. I jest a little – maybe! and there have been benefits of thirty years of child-centred educational policy: students are much less passive than they used to be and they expect their teachers to teach out of their socks, or else ... and certainly stumbling into the classroom with a hangover became less and less possible as the years went by. But I wonder if we have done a service to the current generation by inflating their grades, banning the word 'failure' from their vocabulary and admitting too many of them onto degree courses for which they remain in hock to the tune of 40,000 quid for the rest of their lives. No wonder Generation Rent can't buy property – they're chronically in debt and living at home playing computer games! (On top of that, their profligate Boomer parents have spent the inheritance.)

Felsted was a nationally renowned hockey school with strong cricket and rugby credentials, and I think I was employed to join the hockey staff as much as the English Department. The cricket pro was the wily old former Essex opener Gordon Barker, a man who tended the cricket square with as much zeal as he put into sharing cricket anecdotes and racing tips at the Chequers Inn over a pint (or so) of ale. However, that first summer I was still so much in thrall to my Slavic inamorata that I dodged away from cricket and its attendant time-grabbing commitments so that I could peel off to London for the weekend as soon as the last period of the week was over. This behaviour of mine was considered a bit 'off', and I used to receive knowing looks of disapproval at Monday morning break when all the cricket masters chewed the cud over the weekend's school matches. This, after all, was a school that during the Seventies and Eighties produced three first-class cricketers of note in Derek Pringle, John Stephenson and Nick Knight.

Although my own cricketing activities had temporarily gone the way of 'coupledom' (i.e. the odd snatched session of TV watching the Test during a weekend lull), I became aware of an emergent cricketing star in my youngest English class. In the absence of peremptory government directed assessments for Year 9 in 1978, I was free to indulge my educational whims and decided that my charges could get cracking on their first novel, using up the three sessions a week in which I should probably have been drilling in the five uses of the semi-colon in preference for the quiet hum of composition. There were no howls of outrage from the pupils, fellow teachers, governors of the school or parent body as my class colluded with me in steadily filling their maroon covered exercise books with weekly chapter instalments of their chosen stories. Being a class of boys, most of the stories stumbled on through various unremarkable adventures on imagined battlefields or zapping aliens from outer space; however, one story gripped me from the outset. Narrated (if I remember correctly) in the first person, the opening detailed the life of a cricket-mad schoolboy from a keen games-playing family who had been sent to a school not unlike Felsted. Here he had to deal with the daily grind of academic slog whilst itching to get out into the cricket field to practise for the Colts game against Gresham's on Saturday. Chapter 2 saw his schoolboy star rise when at the age of 14 he was selected for the school 1st XI, having caught the eye of a certain Gordon Barker, who in turn passed on his prowess to the Essex CCC scouts as a promising future prospect. At the County trials he met his hero, Graham Gooch, and vowed to open the innings with him for Essex and, in time, England. No doubt Graham Gooch gave one of his grumpy estuary whines and said something to the effect of 'pull the other one'; or maybe he didn't, but in true Roy of the Rovers style, told young John Stephenson that he admired his 'pluck' and that he looked forward to the day when the two of them would stride out together shoulder to shoulder to open the innings at Chelmsford. By this stage of the novel, I was hooked – particularly when one day he told me that Chapter 2 had already come true. The rest of his novel, minus a few details here and there, pretty much outlined the county and national career (a solitary cap against the Australians in the last Test of 1989) of John Stephenson, Essex, England and MCC Head of Cricket. I bet he was relieved that I didn't try to drill in the five uses of the semi-colon instead. I only wish I had kept his English book – it's an interesting example of how fiction can become fact.

However, with my busy extra-curricular interests taking me down to London at every available opportunity, my life as a cricket tragic was petering out before it had really hit its stride. My sporting life had moved over towards the PE department which was run by the Commonwealth Games gold medallist Alan Lerwill and his sidekick Alasdair Thomson. The new fad at the end of the Seventies was for distance running and the era of the recreational marathon was just around the corner. Rather quixotically, out of the sheer invulnerability that a young man of 25 feels about his physical prowess, I agreed to run as Alasdair's pace-maker in the Harlow Town Marathon of 1980 and hit the infamous 'wall' at twenty miles, collapsing to the ground in a spasm of agony with a gigantic blister weeping pus and blood on my left instep. So much for my dreams of becoming England's next great road-running star.

Before I left Felsted, I had one fortuitous moment of cricketing glory. The 2nd round fixture of the Cricketer Cup was due to be played between the Sherborne Pilgrims and the Felsted Robins at Felsted in late June. Out of the blue I received a phone call that the Pilgrims were a man short and wondered if I would be able to make up the numbers. Ah! the demigods of Sherborne Cricket were grovelling at the feet of one the school's lesser acolytes. I played hard to get for about one second, then jumped at the opportunity to share the turf in my (hastily borrowed) cricket whites with the ageing immortals I'd worshipped in my Sherborne youth. Their gratitude lasted for about a second too before they resumed their drawl about hedge funds, Hunt Balls and the mating rituals of the Hooray Henry. We fielded first and I was consigned to third man and only summoned into the action if they needed cannon fodder at short leg. Felsted posted a respectable score of 174 with Andrew Wingfield-Digby taking

4-48. In reply, Sherborne lost wickets at regular intervals and the innings looked set to peter out. As the seventh wicket fell and I made my way out to the crease, several motor ignitions could be heard to start up as various Sherborne chaps peeled off to make dates back in Chelsea. I then joined Wingfield-Digby in an improbable run chase to victory; at the close he was on 66 and I was on 19. As the ball clattered to the boundary Felstedians emerged from all parts of the campus to witness their school go down to the improbable and treacherous antics of their non-cricketing English teacher. One spectator was Chris Tongue, the Head of Rugby, who three years later was instrumental in getting me a job at Radley by reporting this little cameo of mine to Dennis Silk – an insight into how job interviews used to work and how lives can be changed on the turn of a whim. My response to this euphoric moment of cricketing success was to get legless on quantities of ale in the two local pubs.

The next three years form a shameful blip in my career as a cricket tragic: I failed to play any cricket at all. Instead I moved to London, got married, which is usually a nail in the coffin for any further cricketing life, and researched a thesis on Malcolm Lowry and his 'metaphysical journey' (i.e. massive alcoholic bender undertaken on the lip of a volcano in Mexico). Apart from researching Lowry's first literary footsteps as the hockey correspondent of the school magazine at the Leys School in Cambridge and his self-romanticised portrait of himself as a teenage golfing champion in the Wirral, there was little reference in Lowry's work to balls of any kind, let alone cricket balls, and a lot of drowning in mescal and tequila. I made occasional forays to Lord's and The Oval as a spectator but am forced to admit that the great age of Ian Botham's heroics passed me by. Where were you when England bowled out Australia in the 3rd Test at Headingly for 111? I was in a car driving between Devon and Derby with no access to radio. By the time we moved to Radley in 1983 we had a baby on the way, and it was time to make sure that he/she/it should be birthed into this world in a place where cricket was deemed sacred.

Back to Oxford

My first image of Dennis Silk, the Warden of Radley College, was of his rounding the corner of 'B' Social and peddling along the extensive drive on his bicycle with his gown flapping in the breeze towards where I stood huddled and shivering with nerves in the porch of his imposing residence. When the Quelch-like figure disembarked, my focus was drawn to the extraordinary smile which hovered above his jutting granite jaw. As Scott Fitzgerald wrote about his eponymous and mysterious protagonist Gatsby: 'It was one of those rare smiles with a quality of eternal reassurance in it that you may come across four or five times in a life.' The Gatsby comparison ends there since one of the defining features of this great headmaster was his ability to extend a benevolent and deeply caring interest to the welfare of his whole staff and their families. Like many of the general TV-watching public in 1983, I had been hooked by the 'fly on the wall' documentary series shot at Radley during 1979 and released in 1980. It was the first in a genre of school studies (of both independent and state schools) which have over the years become popular fodder for TV consumption and it was notable for the license given by the school to allow a TV crew to explore the arcane (to most people) world of the privileged elite educated in such institutions with probing frankness. Several reality TV teacher 'stars' were made by the series, but the most fascinating episode focussed on Dennis Silk, who had presided over Radley since 1968 and been forced to confront the moral and social fall-out from the impact of Sixties liberal hedonism upon the traditional austerities of the Victorian public school. The portrait had some quirky moments such as when Dennis examined the fingernails of the newboy intake in chapel and exhorted them to keep them clean as a blueprint for success in life. Imagine watching that as a sink estate 'yoof' in Salford ("yer wot?!"). However, the edgy and in-depth interview which the TV crew recorded with him gave insights into the mind of an educationalist whose exterior conservatism masked an instinctive, creative and flexible grasp of the underlying values which must be at work in any secondary school which addresses the rounded needs of the development of the adolescent towards a mature adulthood. I knew that, when I applied to Radley for the post of English 'don', I would be gaining entry to a great school led by an unique headmaster.

Dennis Silk was a man for whom cricket and literature were inextricably entwined. Another one of these Corinthian athletes who had played cricket for Somerset, led MCC tours abroad, played rugby for Bath and was the national Fives doubles champion for ten years, he was also an English teacher with a great love of Jane Austen and the First World War poets. Indeed, he had befriended and been adopted by the cricket-loving poet Siegfried Sassoon through a mutual acquaintance, another cricket-mad First World War poet Edmund Blunden, and made sure that the war poets were significantly represented in the Radley English curriculum. After half an hour of interview with Dennis, one of the English department dropped by for a pre-prandial sherry (pretty much a de rigueur ritual in those days) before taking me on to lunch and to introduce me to the department. This was Barry Webb, who had been commissioned to write Blunden's biography and later became a tutor at St Peter's College, Oxford. I finally met the head of department, Chris Brown, a man of funereal expression and arid wit, who was soon to leave Radley to become the Head at Norwich school, followed by three hulking great schoolmaster-sportsmen and to round off – in relief – the gifted, friendly and self-deprecating Head of Drama, Jim Hare. Not once was I asked to define my position regarding how to effect value-added learning in the classroom – it was assumed that I would dwell happily with my charges amidst a flurry of war poets and cricket bats.

Snezzy and I (plus future cricketing foetus!) moved from Crouch End to a Radley house on Foxborough Road in the village. At the time the provision of an end-of-terrace house with three small bedrooms and a garden seemed an unimaginable largesse of space to fill, and I can remember the joy at locating a grubby old carpet from a tip which could be spread proprietorially across our bare living room floor. It was a quick hop up to the Radley campus where I inherited a classroom from the outgoing teacher and poet Peter Way, and my first year at Radley was soon underway (again no pun intended).

That first term was surprisingly hard. I was not in practice a complete rookie, having chalked up four years of experience at Felsted, The Lady Eleanor Holles School and Esher Sixth Form College respectively, yet I felt quickly out of my depth. An Oxbridge set of seven sharp young blades proved a handful, and I'm sure that they saw through the rather desperate gobbledygook I served up in my attempt to sound like a 'right on' contemporary scholar. They were kind to me – which was more than they were to the visiting poet P.J. Kavanagh (the English, not the Irish, version) who had just completed a study of the war poet Ivor Gurney and was subjected to a precociously scholarly assault by the Oxbridge seven when it became clear that they could upend his slightly sketchy grasp of various textual details ... the poisonous power of pedantry! However, my real test lay with my form, a Year 11 set composed of ebullient characters who could make or break a newly arrived teacher as easily as snap a twig. The text I had to teach for 'O' Level was Shakespeare's 'The Merchant of Venice'. Not for nothing is it bracketed with Shakespeare's other 'problem plays' as I struggled to elucidate the concepts of Justice and Mercy in 16th century Christian Venice whilst continual ripples of mirth rumbled up from the back row of the classroom whenever I mentioned the names of Bassanio and Antonio (it later transpired that in true puerile fashion the hint of homosexuality in this relationship was a source of embarrassed fascination for these mid-tunnel adolescents. In my paranoid interpretation of their reactions at the time I was convinced that they were mocking my torturous attempts to clarify the concepts at work in the text ...). And not for the first or last time in my teaching career have I reached a point of such benighted despair at my loss of control of a class (sleepless nights, burning the midnight oil with bottle and frantic lesson plan) that I have seriously considered jacking it all in and running off to a commune in Wales.

My saving grace, as it turned out, was my cricket sweater which I wore religiously to class like some sort of protective talisman to ward off evil forces. Unsuspectingly, as the boys' fondness for me grew in inverse relationship to my exasperated incompetence, my desk became the recipient of amateur cartoon sketches of a figure called John Denver beaming with an asinine grin through John Lennon glasses, strumming a guitar and wearing a cricket sweater of varying hues and designs. I've never quite got to the bottom of the John Denver reference (at no other school has there ever been such a supposed likeness ... must have been a passing phase!), but the power of the cricket sweater has endured over the years. Rather like a magician who orchestrates his sleight of hand through diverting the attention of the audience to peripheral phenomena, so my cricket sweater has lured many a generation of youth away from the glaring truth that I might indeed have little of substance to add to their education. Indeed, such was my gratitude to the various incarnations of cricket sweater which have served me through my teaching career that, as I approached my final days at Frensham Heights, I wrote and performed a sketch before the school in which I interviewed my cricket sweater (draped over a chair) for a post as an English teacher. The audience of staff, students and parents were understandably a little perplexed at this self-indulgent piece of solipsism, yet for me it was a timely private rite of passage to celebrate my passing from the classroom.

I knew that I had 'arrived' at Radley when Paul was born on a cold January morning at the start of my second term. The response from both the boys and the community of staff was infectiously warm, and I played off this wave of support to establish myself at the school. The summer term beckoned, and I eagerly anticipated the joys of a first cricket season at Radley. I was given Colts 2 to coach and had mixed feelings when I realised that a substantial number of my Year 11 form were likely to fall under my coaching jurisdiction: jokes about Bassanio and John Denver were now layered with a further cricketing dimension of reference: "Sir, have you ever bowled a maiden over or do you prefer to dangle your tackle outside your off stump? ... chortle chortle ..."

Rather like Eton, the summer sports were divided into 'dry bob' and 'wet bob'. Although the intake of pupils into the school was generally very sporty, it still astonishes me that 600 boys can be divided to spread their talents so evenly over two major sporting pursuits. Over the years, Radley has compiled a distinguished list of both oarsmen and cricketers, and the triumphs on the river have equalled those on the expansive Oxfordshire playing fields where past and recent England cricket captains Ted Dexter and Andrew Strauss learnt their game. Dennis Silk packed his staff with talented schoolmaster-cricketers, but the Club depended upon the partnership between two stalwart professionals – Bert Robinson and Andy Wagner – for its smooth running and the quality of its coaching. Rather quaintly, in a manner reminiscent of the divide that used to exist in cricket circles between the 'amateur gentlemen' and the working-class 'pro', Bert would always address me as 'sir' and request at the beginning of the week what I would like him to prepare for my Colts 2 over the week. Typically, this might include nets on Monday, a shared pitch with Colts 1 on Tuesday, the use of the bowling machine on Thursday and a box net on Friday for pre-match preparation and fielding practice. I often tried to pick up a glimmer of irony in Bert's formal tone of address to me – as it struck me that I was the 'oik' and he was the gentleman in this relationship – but he always kept a straight face. Both Bert and Andy were immensely approachable on any coaching tips that could be passed on, and their legacy to the cricketing reputation of the college has been a long list of cricketers who have gone on to play first-class cricket, notably Andrew Strauss, Robin Martin-Jenkins, Ben Hutton, Jamie Dalyrmple and, more recently, Nick Gubbins.

Ah! The joys of a cricket week at Radley! Every morning the dew would sparkle on the lawn as I made my way to deliver a few lessons of teaching (apologies for waxing lyrical at this point – I guess it was probably often raining ...), followed by the huddle at Common Room break with other cricket dons to discuss likely

Coaching at Radley College – always a joy

team selections for Saturday, then the long afternoon of play and banter with the boys before assembling with colleagues at the Pavilion for the evening staff match against local feeder prep school common rooms such as The Dragon, Summerhill and Ludgrove, rounded off by a sumptuous feast accompanied by fine wines summoned from the college cellar. Meanwhile, our cricket-widow wives (strategically knocked up over last summer's long break) would be too stupefied by the hormonal changes brought on by breeding to reach for the divorce papers and sever all links with their unreconstructed Peter Pan husbands. Saturday was match day and thus sacrosanct: as the busloads of teams embarked for block fixtures against their rivals – Winchester, Eton, Stowe, Harrow and the cream of southern public schools – a palpable frisson spread throughout the school. Runs would be hit, wickets tumble, catches spill, dodgy umpiring decisions prevail, and this was followed by a liquid 'wash-up' enjoyed by all the teacher-coaches at whichever common room was host. Later, I would pore over the scorebook and construct match reports back at home over a final tankard of home brew before steepling into semi-drunken deep sleep – all this after my wife had looked after the children all day whilst I was 'hard at work'.

Sunday should have been a sacrosanct family day. However, the local village team were always on the prowl for staff members to swell their ranks for Sunday games. Their ring-leader was one of the College groundsmen, Jeff Grimes, who would subtly inveigle himself into the households of cricketing dons, offering to cut their lawn cheaply in return for cricketing favours. Every week, after we had moved from Foxborough Road into a larger house at the gates of the campus called The Lodge, Jeff would pop his head over the hedge and whisper to me: "Hey, Mark, your missus at 'ome? Fancy playin' Buscot Park on Sunday? We need an allrounder." No sooner had he posed his request than a strident voice would bawl out from inside the entrails of the house: "Mark! Where are you? Simon's nappy needs changing!" Jeff would duck his head and wink at me: "Orr roight, Mark, just to let you know ... Two o'clock start on the Junior Colts square. I'll just give your lawn a trim tomorrow after work to keep your missus sweet." I must confess that many a 'don' had a much less understanding wife. Nevertheless, the pleasure of playing cricket with the local community folk was as much to do with fostering relationships outside of the Radley 'bubble' as escapism from domestic duty. I still have a booklet in which I religiously kept all my statistics for Radley Village spanning over a decade's worth of play: how tragic is that?

Meanwhile the personnel in the English Department changed. Chris Brown and Barry Webb had left, and two new arrivals appeared: the brilliant and combative Bernard O'Keefe who would later become Head of Sixth Form at St Paul's and the softly-spoken poet-editor Simon Lewis. We were a young and rudderless department so Dennis Silk appointed Christopher Dixon to run the show in a gamble that we would 'gell' around a man whose legendary intellectual brilliance preceded him. After a meteoric career through the English departments of Oakham and Eton, Christopher Dixon had taken on a headmastership at Cobham Hall, a girls' school in Kent, a role for which this shy, introverted maverick had hardly been suited. Dennis caught him in freefall from this disaster and installed him at Radley in the hope that he could re-route his career more appropriately. Things started swimmingly and, like young puppies, we lapped up Christopher's erudite and barely understood conversational asides, and we also leapt at the challenges he posed us (one of these was to introduce the first year Shell intake to a history of literary theory from Leavis through to Derrida – we managed to persuade him that perhaps this might appeal more to a sixth form, if not a university seminar). However, it soon became clear that all was not well. He developed a nervous apprehension of turning up to school and, if you caught sight of him on campus, he would scurry off in the opposite direction. He often called in absent ill, and there were rumours circulating that he was a member of the extreme Catholic sect Opus Dei, who practise purifying rituals of self-mortification of the flesh. One day we turned up to the department in the morning to be told the tragic news that Christopher Dixon had committed suicide. The autopsy revealed an overdose, and the background pathology painted a sad picture of a man who had struggled both with depression and engagement with reality over several years. His brief tenure at Radley was the tail-spin of a much longer process of decline. Nevertheless, we were all deeply shocked and wondered if there was anything we could have done to help.

Mostly, I found my professional life at Radley deeply satisfying during the first eight years. Apart from the sport and the teaching, there was a wide selection of extra-curricular clubs and societies on offer, and it is really this dimension of an education that an all-boarding school can excel at. One day I was approached by one of my pupils who clearly enjoyed being in my class, Andrew Hunt, and asked if I would chair the newly hatched Tintin Society. I knew little and cared even less about Herge's be-quiffed boy sleuth, but Andrew's obvious enthusiasm persuaded me that my only role would be to make my study available as a meeting ground along with a keg of the potent home brew refreshments for which I was renowned. The society's meetings were initially viewed with some tolerant scepticism but the ranks of members soon swelled, a special member's tie was commissioned and housemasters would often phone through to me before House Check-in to enquire as to the whereabouts of one of their charges. Furthermore, the intellectual quality of the membership escalated as the sharpest Oxbridge candidates were lured into vying to outwit each other with pretentious but exacting theses for their talks, such as 'A feminist critique of Herge's protagonist' and 'Post-colonial readings of Tintin in Tibet'. The Director of Studies was suddenly edging up to me at Short Break to ask whether so-and-so should be advised to go for Oxford or Cambridge. Yes, 'Tintin in Radley' was a going concern ... until tragedy struck. One Saturday afternoon Andrew and one of his friends managed to persuade a car dealer to let them test-drive a turbo-charged vehicle on the Oxford Ring Road. Andrew lost control of the wheel and swerved over the middle (at the one point where no crash barrier existed) into an oncoming car. All the passengers in both vehicles were killed instantly, and the body parts were virtually unidentifiable.

Radley was also a wonderful place to pursue an interest in racquet sports. The school pro was Mick Dean, a top-flight real tennis player, who ran the rackets teams as well as real tennis, lawn tennis and doubling up in the Geography and Modern Languages departments. For anyone whose blood thrills to the thwack of racquet on ball, rackets is the superlative sport and the ultimate test of eye/hand co-ordination. Originating as a pre-cursor to its counterpart squash, rackets was first played in the 19th Century by prisoners in the debtor's courts in London. Soon it caught on at Harrow school and has subsequently been played by a select few public schools. The distinguishing features are a cottage-industry-crafted hard ball, an elongated racquet and a court twice the dimensions of a squash court. The ball moves at terrifying speeds of up to 170 mph, and players need to meet the ball with a classical stance or it will literally sheer off the back and side wall and take your head off. Mick very kindly allowed me (and a few other enthusiasts; I ran the Squash Club at the time) to take up the game in a rudimentary fashion, and it certainly widened my repertoire of ball sports in an exciting way. The world rackets champion at the time was an old Radleian called James Male and it was a real privilege to be able to watch him shift the ball around the court with such elegance and power whenever he played at Radley.

Apart from playing for the Village, I used to turn out for the Sherborne Pilgrims when they had a fixture against the Radley Rangers. With the amount of cricket that I was playing and my familiarity with the batting-friendly Radley squares, I regularly pitched in with some useful scores in front of 'discerning' viewers. I was approached and asked if I would like to trial for the Free Foresters, the ultimate dream for the 'not quite good enough but not a bad player' category of cricketer to which I belonged. The procedure was that your name would be forwarded by a current member and that you would be summoned to play in three games, and if successful, receive an invitation to take up life-long membership (so that as the years rolled by you could snobbishly point at your tie in any cricketing gathering and feel like 'one of the chaps'). I duly found myself selected to play for the Free Foresters against the Radley 1st XI on Sunday 22 April 1990 (I snaffled the team sheet from the notice-board and am sadly perusing its yellowing details as I write). The team was filled with redolent names: former county batsman Ian Peck coming in at number three whilst I was sandwiched at number six between Neil Durden-Smith and Christopher Martin-Jenkins. We batted first, and I made my way out to the centre to meet the ball which would either propel me into the dizzy echelons of Free Forester cricket dressing rooms around the country or send me back to my village grassroots. Alas, the ball swerved through bat and pad and clattered into the stumps and I was never approached by the Free Foresters again. However, on my death bed, I may yet croak out my final line: "I was a Free Forester once ... the rest is silence."

In my pomp

The tide turned on my Radley career after Dennis Silk retired in 1991. He had been Warden of the College for 23 years, and I guess the time had come for a change of leadership style, even if the successful formula was to be kept the same. It was an unenviable task to follow Warden Silk's reign, but the man selected for the task had been one of Dennis's housemasters and had just completed a successful spell as Headmaster of Cheltenham College, Richard Morgan. Was it wise to appoint someone who still had relatively fresh connections to Radley? Was it possible on the other hand for any outsider to fill Dennis's boots? I don't know. However, as for me, a cool breeze could be detected in the cloisters. I'd reached my mid- to late-thirties and I was, as one very literal-minded colleague informed me one day, "a non-specific person". I was neither a housemaster nor a head of department, and there appeared to be no obvious career progression at Radley in sight. I had even ticked off the teacher exchange year with another school in U.S.A. Was I already at my still relatively tender age beginning to smell of washed-up dead wood?

In 1991 many public schools were beginning to feel the 'sword of Damocles' hovering over their financial status. Post-Thatcher Britain had put the squeeze on middle-class Britain, and the clientele who could afford the exorbitant fees of a British boarding-school education was changing. Independent schools had to market themselves as brands in a competitive corporate market, and dear old Mr Chips had better sharpen up his act or the inspectors would consign him to the knackers. The first sign of change came from Morgan's opening speech to Common Room in which he etched out a vision of future Radleians marching into Europe and the Far East to nail down pan-global corporate ventures in foreign markets (I guess it was just 19th Century Imperialism re-hashed for the late 20th Century, even if the points of reference had changed). Smart members of staff quickly realised that, to stake your claim in the new Radley, you had to dress like a corporate lawyer, brandish a little red handkerchief out of your top pocket and stride purposefully from A to B with a briefcase; idiots like me continued to wear their cricket sweaters off the cricket field, failed to knot up their top buttons and still smudged chalk on their jackets.

During the next four years, Morgan tightened his squeeze on me as well as several other colleagues who wore the wrong face, and I found myself in a difficult spot. I had a young family of four children to support, no house or financial savings to retreat to, should the worst come to the worst, and I could feel the carpet being gently but inexorably shifted from under my feet. Eventually the stress drove me to a painful episode of depression from which recovery was slow. The final nail in my coffin was the appointment of a new young head of department, freshly sourced along a perfect CV conveyor belt: Oxford, Marlborough and Eton. Aged only 33 and very ambitious, he wanted to mould his own department and wasn't going to bide his time and work with the given material. I can recall his technique for 'getting to know' his department. He decided to pair up with each of us in turn and observe our approaches as we gave the Oxbridge students a tutorial. Somewhat unwisely, when my turn popped up, I chose a Vaughan poem and started to unpick busily the neo-Platonic imagery in 'The Waterfall' with what I thought was scholarly precision. Suddenly the discussion was batted aside with a wafting arc of an arm and a sigh of irritation: "Yes, this is all very well, but what about Ennui?" Two students looked up from the text quizzically. "Yes, Ennui," he continued. "The condition which swept across the salons of Europe during the early 19th Century. We should be looking at the powerful movements which defined European culture during the last two centuries … all those troubled young intellectuals restless and bored, striving for change." Without risking rudeness and conscious of the puzzlement of the students, I tried to suggest that perhaps Ennui and neo-Platonic thought were unlikely bedfellows. Not long after this incident, cut-outs of T.E.S. English job vacancies started to appear in my pigeon-hole, and pointed references were made about my plans for career progression. There is nothing more deconstructive of self than constructive dismissal.

Going West to the Cotswolds

It was quite an upheaval to gather up twelve years of residence at Radley to move to an area none of us knew. Paul and Natasha had to be extricated from the Dragon School, and the whole family was now bound for Wycliffe College, nestling at the confluence of the Five Valleys near Stroud. As opposed to the fashionable North Cotswolds beloved of media folk seeking a designer rural weekend retreat from frenetic London lifestyles, the South Cotswolds is a hive of local crafts and produce, green politics and artists retreating into various stages of hippy 'begrizzledom'. Still home to an ageing Laurie Lee in his beloved Slad Valley, this was 'Cider with Rosie' country on hash, forming the tip of the West Country mystical leyline which cuts diagonally from Stroud through Glastonbury to Totnes: feel the vibe!

I had managed to secure one of those TES jobs placed in my pigeon hole and was now at the age of 40 poised to run my own English department. Stepping out from Radley to Wycliffe was like exchanging a Rolls Royce for a Skoda. However, I quickly appreciated that Wycliffe had a lot to recommend it. An unpretentious and friendly school with a Methodist foundation and a history of quirky sandal-wearing vegetarianism, it served the local Stroud Valleys' middle-class community well; nevertheless, it was struggling in a financial world where powerful neighbouring schools in Cheltenham and Bristol carved out the choice cuts in the market. Battling to assert its individuality in the marketplace, the new headmaster David Prichard (a restless maverick entrepreneur who had just retired from jazzing up Port Regis school and needed a retirement project) had embarked on a kooky advertising campaign in which he commissioned billboards with depictions of cows and the logo 'Wycliffe the pre-University College of the Cotswolds' to be placed at strategic viewing points on the M5 motorway. He also established 'squash scholarships' and opened the college's doors to overseas students in an indiscriminate manner (no Brexit for him!) so that the campus rang with the mixed medley of Cantonese, Russian and the local Gloucestershire soft burr. A hastily assembled EFL department had been whisked into place and was already the largest department in the college. My job was somehow to keep the flame of 'A' Level English Literature scholastics alight whilst adapting to the unrealistic demands of ambitious overseas students who expected to fly through to English universities with cobbled-together English fluency skills. Luckily, the school could employ Snezzy's teaching and EFL background, and the presence of an attached junior school meant that all four children could be educated at staff-reduced fee rates in the same location.

Despite its small size, Wycliffe had produced its fair share of cricketers over the years. There were Charlie Barnett and Gilbert Parkhouse, both of whom played for England, and the school boasted the Gidman brothers, Alex and Will, amongst its current pupils. The cricket facilities were modest compared to Radley, but the location at the pivotal apex of England around the Severn estuary meant that in every direction the school had access to opponents in Wales, the West Country and east along the M4 corridor: it felt like the quiet heart of rural southern England. In my first summer term I was given the Under-15s to look after. There was only one problem: the squad consisted of five Europeans and seven from the Pacific rim. After some consultation with the powers that be (who were alarmed at the potentially embarrassing marketing fall-out, should the school fail to fulfil its traditional fixture list commitments), it was agreed that one APR Gidman should be kept down to captain his age group rather than play up in the 1st XI where his natural ability belonged. And thus the weekly gamble began: if Gidman scored a century and took ten wickets, Wycliffe won; anything less than 50 and he'd struggle to peg back more than three or four of the opposition; if he scored zero then we were reliant upon a few face-saving snicks through the slips from some inscrutable flashing swipes from a lower order oriental blade. Even Alex Gidman couldn't keep wicket to his own bowling. For him it was a good training ground in diplomacy and expediency from which Gloucestershire and England A were to reap the later rewards.

Both Paul and Simon were coming to an age when the prospect of accompanying me to watch first-class games began to appeal. We started off by supporting Somerset down at Taunton where we cheered on 'Mooshy' (Mushtaq Ahmed) and enjoyed Trescothick clattering the ball around the park – which he continues to do in 2018. Then we switched our allegiance to our new home county Gloucestershire which had an unfashionable team but was the first county side to really crack the requirements of limited-overs pyjama cricket. Thanks to the brilliant and highly eccentric wicket-keeping of Jack Russell and the inspirational leadership of 'BooBoo' Alleyne and

Our hero, Jack Russell of Gloucestershire and England, with Simon

coach John Bracewell, a team of journeymen had been honed into the finest fielding side in the land (and probably the world). Gloucestershire had always managed to recruit overseas players who became dedicated to the county (Mike Proctor, Zaheer Abbas and Sadiq Mohammad back in the 70s and 80s); now the county had the great West Indian quick Courtney Walsh and Craig Spearman from New Zealand to help galvanise a bunch of local boys into one of the most successful one-day teams ever, winning several tournaments which we witnessed at Bristol, Cheltenham and Lord's, chanting "Glosturr Glosturr" in broad West Country accents as a chicken was mysteriously tossed around the crowd (I never quite got to the bottom of that chicken!). By this stage Paul was a keen follower of the game, but Simon was still very young and found the intervals in play when he could charge about the outfield and throw a ball around more entertaining than the play itself, so to combat his restlessness we used to bribe him with sweets and ice creams if he could 'last out till the next over'.

One of the pay-offs for fathering sons always seemed to me to be the chance to perhaps play Father-and-Son cricket one day. Of course, all parties must be willing and competent to effect this. Luckily, both Paul and Simon were keen and able cricketers from the outset. I knew from our early games of garden cricket – populated with such legendary and inexplicable fantasy figures as 'Robot Tom', 'Whirling Dervish' and 'The Withered Arm' – that they would be ready to join me on the field of battle on village greens when they hit their teenage years.

Stroud Valleys cricket is defined by its undulant geography. Clubs nestled into the sides of valley escarpments and eked out cricket squares at gradients which inevitably perched sloping on the edge of a steep decline. Any ball struck too hard might roll off down the valley through a field of sheep and end up on the counter of 'The Butcher's Arms', the pub adjacent to Laurie Lee's ground at Sheepscombe. This meant that the main pre-requisite of village cricketers was a resolute sense of the absurd, and thankfully there were relatively few pompous anal-retentives trying to protect their batting and bowling averages. I was drawn to the Men of Horsley partly because it was the most local team, but also because it consciously punned with Menopausal. The make-up of the side, led by a portly psychotherapist who was obsessed with his achievement of once being selected for Yorkshire Schools Under 15s, was bohemian and eclectic, populated with artists, writers, teachers and rat-race escapees. The banter was as sharp and witty as the cricketing prowess was flawed (our keeper, local landscape artist Anthony Hodge, prided himself on being the top scorer with the number of byes he let through in an innings). In such company the team was grateful for the spine of competence which the Floyer father-and-son combo provided. We were not the most prolific banterers, but I could usually be counted on to post a decent score and Paul would often scythe through sides with his deceptively wobbly off-cutters (to even greater effect if Anthony Hodge had ever held on to a catch! "Sorry, Paul old chap, didn't want to blemish the record ... I'll snaffle the next one – promise!").

One summer a blowsy young librarian with a roguish eye joined the staff at Wycliffe. In the common room at break time she would seek out the cricket corner and try to join in the conversation whilst crossing and uncrossing her legs and massaging her cleavage into various eye-popping vistas. It transpired that she was (in her own words) a voracious cricket scorer and was looking for action around the Stroud Valleys ... she said she was quite happy to come and spend all Saturday afternoon with her selection of multi-coloured pens and scorebook if the captain might occasionally select her recently hitched-on and already beleaguered husband. Her only stipulation was that she be allowed to wear figure-hugging outfits and flirt flagrantly with any pair of white trousers which caught her fancy. This was not good news for the menopausal men of the Stroud Valleys trying desperately to keep their marriages afloat and their mortgages paid whilst indulging in a little harmless all-male recreation on the weekend. Suddenly married club members were mysteriously whisked off on 'family duty', immaculately scribed scorecards began to tell a woeful tale of underachievement, local gym bunny lotharios who had shunned cricket as a game for nancy boys now eagerly enquired about club subscription rates, and after-match drinks dissolved into a welter of innuendo. Disaster! My closest shave with temptation came on one Friday afternoon when we had an evening game over at Cranham. The librarian suggested that she drive me from school to the Cranham ground and then drop me off afterwards at home, perhaps (she archly suggested) popping in for a swift drink at The Old Lodge Inn on Minchinhampton Common on the way back. Good Angel and Bad Angel loomed over left and right shoulder! "Go on," said Bad Angel, "life's an adventure ... take your chances!" "!!!!! ... Caveat," replied Good Angel, "nothing beats a clear conscience," so Good Angel arranged for the wife to accompany this particular cricketing 'jolly' in order that Mr Midlife Crisis could sit on the fence and keep his conscience intact whilst the librarian had a sulk (not for long – one of the Cranham players bought her a drink and she was soon avidly sizing up the statistics of the opposition!).

Compared to the hazards of local cricket, running the English department was precarious but rewarding. The staffing combinations year in year out ran through all sorts of permutations so that I found myself by default carrying the show on my own back. The general lack of prurient eyes scrutinising my every move gave me an unexpected freedom to embrace my private passions. I chose to channel the department budget into bringing poets such as Jon Silkin, Jenny Joseph, UA Fanthorpe and Philip Gross on to campus to give workshops and readings rather than stock up the bookshelves with expensive text books with yawn-inducing titles such as 'GCSE success, a course in ten stages'. My line manager, Mike Scott-Baumann, was a fiery and accomplished historian and intellectual whose leadership of the school academics was always cavalier rather than roundhead, so that I was given free rein to turn Wycliffe into a poetry school.

Encouraged by Jenny Joseph, who lived up the road in Minchinhampton, I was also writing a lot of poetry at this stage and placing work with the little magazines (of varying quality and repute) which make England such a fertile place to be a scribbler. I started up a magazine called Konfluence on a cottage-industry basis and was soon over-run with submissions from around the world. The magazine ran to six issues and garnered a lot of praise in its short lifespan, and there is even a boxfile in the Poetry Library at the South Bank which lovingly preserves all six editions for posterity. Through the magazine I encountered several poets with whom I was to collaborate. There was BZ Niditch from Boston, a prolific minor New England poet who was a member of the famous class Robert Lowell ran at Harvard in 1959 which included the emergent talents of Sylvia Plath and Anne Sexton. Together we brought out a shared pamphlet entitled 'Thinking Englandly and New Englandly'. Closer to home I came into the orbit of influence of the small press 'tyro' Barry Tebb who published three of my pamphlets in his Sixties Press imprint and anthologised me in 'Orphans of Albion: Poetry of the British Underground'. After six years at Wycliffe (following twelve at Radley) I was road-wrecked by the classroom and in need of a break, so I followed my enthusiasms for creative writing with a year's sabbatical, signing up to do a Masters course at Cardiff University before putting my head back in the noose at Ardingly College.

Decline and Fall in the Cradle of Cricket

Ardingly is set in some of the most beautiful countryside in southern Britain – a paradise in mid-Sussex nestling close to the Downs. The school itself is a somewhat forbidding Victorian pile, built around an ornate High Anglican chapel. From the outset I had an uneasy feeling about this place. There was something about the architecture which made people feel defensive and burrow off into the labyrinth of passages which wound through its interior. This was a perfect location for breeding cliques and whispered gossip and perpetrating acts of cruelty which would go undetected behind closed doors. Yes! After a year of being a middle-aged student, I was reluctantly back in the saddle!

The school is part of the Woodard Foundation and was being brought to heel after a slightly chaotic period by the flinty-souled Australian disciplinarian John Franklin. Why he appointed me, I don't know. He was clearly looking for a thick-skinned middle-manager who could bully the department of dinosaur English teachers into submission and crack the English classes into shape. Well, fair enough! But why me? I can't even pretend to be scary at interview. It wasn't long before I was miserable, ill and yearning for that commune in Wales. The one plus was that his wife Kim (a very gifted sixth Form teacher) was implementing the International Baccalauriat into the department, and I was soon a fan of this broad-minded curriculum for international students.

Luckily, Ardingly had a great reputation as a football school and Simon was a keen and talented footballer. The other three children had progressed on to Marlborough for their secondary schooling, but Ardingly was just right for Simon, who played in the Gothia Cup in Sweden as a thirteen-year-old and whose subsequent career as a footballer was stymied by the diagnosis of Crohn's disease a year later. Snezzy also loved teaching at Ardingly and became one of the key figures on the staff, so I guess it was just me who had an adverse reaction to the perceived oppressiveness of the school's ambience. Ideally I would have packed in schoolmastering after Wycliffe ... but there were bills to meet and no-one was interested in paying an obscure poetaster for his scribbled verses, alas.

As ever, Cricket came to the rescue. Visit any village playing field in the south-east of England on a Friday evening in early summer, and the chances are that you'll find it populated with scores of youngsters being coached by enthusiastic amateur coaches. This, after all, is the cradle of cricket where the noble game first sprang (first reference being to a game of 'creckett' being played in 1550 in Guildford), and it remains very popular in the region despite the preference of youth culture for Premier League Football and their mobiles. The nearest ground was adjacent to our garden at Ansty, and so I started to attend the weekly nets and begin the laborious process of convincing the club selectors that I was worth more than an outing at number nine with an outside chance of a bowl at the end of the innings. I also decided, emerging from a winter of depression, to treat myself to a new bat for the first time in my life. Wisdom Sports in Haywards Heath was owned by the son of the comedian Norman Wisdom, who prided himself on his cricket workshop in which he prepared and knocked in bespoke bats. I chose a Salix and waited for the seasoning of the willow to be completed before trying it out in the nets. It was the most beautifully balanced bat I had ever played with, light in the pick-up but resonant with power in its middle. I just needed to find an opportunity to use it.

The sun shone on an end-of-term afternoon as the Ardingly staff took on the 1st XI for the annual showcase against the school's best – a match played with some indulgent good spirit but with competitive needle underneath. In the absence of any takers, I found myself walking out to the square to open the innings, proudly bearing my polished Salix sabre in my hand and hoping that I would at least avoid the ignominy of a duck. Twenty overs later, after an hour of swatting the ball to all parts of the field, I had carved my way to my first and only ton. When you're 'in the zone' (and this is very rare for me), the ball swells to the size of a football and you can cuff it about with laughable ease as all the fielders collude with you by dropping the catches you pepper them with. Why does the ball shrink to the size of an invisible pellet when you next go in to bat? Anyway, I returned to the pavilion in a state of shock, and there in the immaculate scoring script of Mrs Brown (mother of the talented Sussex captain and keeper-batsman Ben Brown) lay the evidence of my triumph. A year later I was to repeat the performance, reaching 80 not out, so that my tally as I went in to my third year was 180 not out: I duly scored a duck to give me an average of 180 in Staff vs Pupil matches. Beat that, Sachin!

Sussex was also a haven of women's cricket with Clare Connor, the England captain of the time, teaching at Brighton College and grooming a generation of talented women cricketers on the south coast. Simon had the pleasure of hitting Holly Colvin, the future England leg-spinner, for a boundary in an under-14 game against Brighton (before she trapped him next ball) whilst I witnessed at first hand the prodigious wicket-keeper/batting talents of future England star Sarah Taylor when umpiring an Under-15 game. I have since been converted to the attractions of women's cricket and will regularly tune into the highlights of matches on TV. Unlike the men's game which has developed into a frenzy of unorthodox power-hitting through the popular 20/20 format, the women's game is still by comparison slower and more sedate. However, the skills with which they play are classically orthodox, and it is almost like being re-wound to a previous age when the likes of Colin Cowdrey would incise the field with elegant and perfectly placed cover drives – an aesthetic delight at its best.

It was after the 'heroics' of my century against the boys that I was approached by a member of staff and asked if I would like to play for his team, Staplefield. His daughter Yvann was a pupil at Ardingly and about to start the IB in the sixth form, and an accomplished all-round cricketer who played for the village (later she was to earn a blue at Oxford). What? Was I being 'poached' from Ansty? My head swelled. Of course I would bequeathe my stupendous cricketing talents to Staplefield and at no cost too!

Winston Churchill's grandson opens the new Staplefield pavilion

And thus began five years of dedicated village cricket on one of the most delightful grounds in the cradle of cricket. Perched on an incline, Staplefield's ground was flanked on either end by a pub ('The Victory' at the top and 'The Jolly Tanners' at the bottom) so that players could keep themselves perpetually 'oiled', dipping in and out for refreshment as the contours of the game unfolded and released a spare moment to indulge.

Is it possible to become a better player in your late forties and early fifties? The answer is probably 'only if you take up the game in your mid forties'! There's no accounting for the loss of reaction speed, muscle flexibility and acuteness of eyesight which sets in for most cricketers in their mid- to late-thirties. However, the passing of time undoubtedly improves the temperament and inculcates a stoicism about outcome which helps you to focus on what is achievable rather than falling victim to the mood swings which accompany this most fickle of games. I had always been a high-energy all-rounder who threw himself into all aspects of the game in the hope that I would at least pick up a wicket or two, thrash a speedy thirty or snaffle a catch in the slips. Now as my body stiffened with incipient age, I needed to marshall my resources more carefully and discover my 'inner Boycott'. I took to opening the innings, occupying the crease, calculating percentages and nurdling singles through second slip and gully with soft hands. I think I probably became a better cricketer week in week out than I had been in youth, even if I could no longer pick up balls moving at speed and hoik them across the line over mid-wicket. I certainly spent more time in the middle than in my early days.

On the father-and-son front, the focus had moved from Paul to Simon. Paul had decided to trade in his bat for an electric guitar and was fronting up a heavy metal band called 'Morningsidespeed', named somewhat alarmingly after the term used amongst Glasgow heroin addicts for the first hit of the day. The band had a short but successful lifespan, becoming a fixture on the Bristol gig circuit for a year or two. Simon, meanwhile, was developing into a hard-hitting batsman and played for an Ardingly 1st XI against the MCC at the age of 14. His real strength lay in his outfielding where he could throw himself about in the chase and rocket in balls over the top of the stumps with great accuracy (into the safe gloves of Ben Brown). One day I was phoned up by an Ardingly Modern Languages teacher who played for Haywards Heath and asked if I could turn out with my two sons: a fearsome Floyer triumvirate was summoned to put to the sword the visitors from nearby Horsham. He knew about Simon and me but was in awe of the 'other' Floyer who, of course, I had 'bigged up' as a former teen prodigy who had tragically been lost from the game to the high-decibel clutches of Heavy Metal! We three were inserted at the top of the order and made 4, 0, and 0 respectively. Much to the consternation of the Modern Languages teacher, who had by now wound himself up into a self-destructive frenzy, we then buttered several catches through our fingers when we fielded and the match was duly lost. The father-and-son

*Father and son cricket – the day we distinguished ourselves
for Haywards Heath against Horsham*

triumvirate has never been summoned into action again, and now awaits the emergence of a next-generation Floyer in about fifteen years' time to restore honour to the family cricketing reputation. I may even be tempted into action from grandfatherly retirement, should the call come!

Meanwhile the English teaching was going from bad to worse. Despite acquiring a freak accumulation of A* grades with a difficult top set (an achievement attributed by the headmaster to the fortuitous incompetence of the exam boards rather than any magic I might have imparted), I was steadily being penned in for the chop. Ordered to attend his study one day, I was charged with the accusation that my head-of-department budget plan could be fitted onto the back of a postage stamp, to which I facetiously replied that I found that working in enclosed parameters concentrated the mind wonderfully, to which the headmasterly retort was that, to paraphrase Dr Johnson, 'Execution' had the same efficacious power upon the mind. An Exit sign beamed up above the headmaster's study door, pointing to the school gates, and I wandered desultorily around the grounds on a damp November afternoon considering what the future could possibly bring next.

The answer was into the proverbial frying pan from the fire! During the latter stages of my demise at Ardingly I had fallen prey to a series of Larkinesque St Trinian's themed fantasies. A common scenario would depict me perched in a huddle of a spellbound comely girls whilst I mesmerised them with a reading of Coleridge's 'Kubla Khan': his flashing eyes, his floating hair! Afterwards they would pet my ageing locks in gratitude before gambolling off to the lacrosse pitch squealing with high-spirited laughter. Yes, I confess I started to scan the TES for a job in a girls' school where I fondly imagined I could play out the dotage of my teaching career amongst the appreciative and indulgent murmurs of civilised young females.

Wrong! St Leonard's-Mayfield is a prominent Catholic girls' school in East Sussex. However, the teaching nuns had long since retreated into their cloisters in flight from the belligerent noises of 20th century feminism. On my first entry into the classroom I became aware of a low-level titter of giggles. This erupted into a paroxysm of contorted bodies and hysterical laughter as soon as I opened my mouth to say: "Now, girls ..." Here was a new type of discipline problem, the like of which I had never encountered before. What do you do when twenty girls collapse into helpless laughter every time you speak? I tried the reasonable approach – "OK, girls, I know you think I'm wearing a funny white sweater with stripes, but let's get serious now ...", then the enforced silence where I froze in effigy awaiting the abatement of their response (this provoked a tsunami of hilarity), followed, I regret to say, by the throathoarsening roar: "Shhuuuut uuuupp!!!" (you're doomed as a classroom practitioner at this point) which usually necessitated the intervention of a poker-faced teacher from next door who'd silence the class instantly with one beady eye cast across the room.

In co-educational contexts, girls tend to be the 'mature' influence for the good over rather 'immature' boys. Allow them to entertain a male teacher in their own collective stronghold, however, and they can destroy every vestige of your self-respect. As a form master, one of my designated tasks was to check that the girls wore their uniform with suitable decorum. Every morning I had to spot-check their attire to make sure that the Virgin Mary couldn't take offence at any evidence of secular sartorial influences which might have besmirched their pure and receptive minds and souls overnight. A young minx (who shall remain nameless) used to sidle up to my chair, dangle her crucifix suggestively over her low-cut cleavage with purple-painted fingernails and then hitch up her low-cut skirt to reveal an inch of bare flesh pinched between a hitched-up stocking and a pair of crotch-splitting thongs. With an insouciant stare she would then coo: "Everything OK for sir?"

After two years of being fed to the lionesses' den, I developed a severe bout of pleurisy, followed by a further depressive episode. Surely I had completed the final 'infra dig' penances of my teaching career – or had I? There remained only one type of school which I had not sampled. Ever since watching a TV documentary of A.S. Neill's alternative school Summerhill, I had fancied my chances amidst a maelstrom of liberal anarchy. Frensham Heights, Bedales' slightly overlooked sister school, was advertising for an English teacher and I sent in my letter of application promptly. I arrived for interview at a beautiful mansion on the Surrey/Hampshire border and walked past a bizarre wire-meshed installation of a rabbit on the front lawn. The headmaster, Andrew Fisher, offered me a tray of jellybeans at interview and fired a few left-field questions at me. It felt like I'd been sucked into 'Alice in Wonderland' as he outlined his ideal teaching zone in the woods where teachers and students could cavort in a merry dance of kinaesthetic creativity in a specially designed tree-house classroom. I wanted the job but alas came second in the interview stakes.

Two months later Andrew Fisher contacted me again to ask if I was still interested in coming to Frensham. Another English teacher had resigned so that a fresh vacancy existed, should I still be interested. The two outgoing teachers were veteran Frenshamians who had both earned legendary reputations for their eccentricities. I can only think that I was employed on the basis that my relatively advanced age would act as some sort of continuum from their double act. And so we upped sticks and moved across from mid-Sussex to the Surrey/ Hampshire border.

Founded in 1925 by two sisters steeped in theosophical ideas, the school was one of several institutions which sprang up at the start of the 20th century in opposition to the prevailing 'hale and hearty' ethos of the traditional Victorian public school. Teachers and pupils were set on equal footing, addressed each other by their Christian names, there was no mandatory school uniform, attendance at lessons was optional, and competition in sports was banned. The school possessed a strong social conscience and provided a haven for Jewish refugees from Nazi Germany, as well as being a place where the Arts were passionately pursued. The type of pupil it attracted either came from high-minded Bloomsbury-style thinkers or were misfits from unconventional homes. If you scan the list of famous alumni you will find amidst a list of arty types a notable fraudster, a bounty hunter, an illusionist and a complete dearth of soldiers and captains of industry. The school underwent an 'interesting' 1960s and 1970s and had continued to plough a private furrow of obscure whimsy on the edge of the independent sector. When I arrived in 2007, the 'ethos' was being subtly tightened up by Andrew Fisher whose cultivated 'wacky' exterior concealed an educationalist well versed in implementing prescriptive policies in more orthodox institutions. To be fair, he was responding to market forces and making sure that Frensham rode out the latest recession and attracted middle-class parents who wanted a mix of conventional exam success delivered in a casing of acceptable kooky informality.

For about four years I revelled in the liberating atmosphere that allowed me to work in a school where most teaching practices were licensed, provided they were underpinned by wholesome creative objectives. The close and friendly relationships encouraged between staff and pupils led me to initiate all sorts of creative endeavours with some genuinely gifted students. Furthermore, the head of sixth form at the time, Jonny Warner, was a charismatic and visionary educationalist who brought me into the fold and delegated to me a lot of very interesting work with the sixth-formers. However, the other side of this idyllic package was that many of the lower-school students just couldn't cope with the demands of such creative freedom. It quickly transpired at parents' evenings that Little Freddy, attired in his distressed jeans and baseball cap slung around the wrong way, was perhaps not a budding creative genius but in truth a vulnerable and cossetted boy with learning difficulties sent to Frensham by anxious middle-class parents ever hopeful that he could be nursed towards the same examination outcomes as their more conventionally competent sibling sent to Charterhouse.

Whilst the standards of Dance, Drama, Music and Art were extremely high, the cricket at Frensham was a tad lackadaisical. Floppy-haired boys would turn up for practice and quickly tire of chasing a cricket ball, preferring to sit on the boundary and weave daisy chains. Much as I was ready in some respects to wallow in the whole hippy 'schtick', when it came to cricket I still yearned to play to competitive rules and within competitive contexts. Once again I was on the lookout for a club to play for. The l'Anson cricket league spreads across a radius of Surrey, Hampshire and Sussex and is reputedly the oldest continuous village league in England and thus probably the world. It was founded at Grayshott in January 1901 and has flourished ever since. Being an obsessive grass-roots cricket addict, I quickly beat my path to the door of Grayshott CC headquarters and offered them the remaining good years of my geriatric cricketing lifespan.

It is a tremendous family club which runs four competitive adult teams on Saturdays and a host of youth teams coached by dedicated parents and older club members. I found myself opening the innings for the 3rd XI which gave me the chance to bring on some talented youngsters as they made their way up to the 1st XI, a source of great satisfaction. The teams were also multi-age, ranging from youngsters of 12 to the redoubtable Alan Lang who would week-in-/week-out bowl a twenty-over spell at the age of 75. My best year was 2010, and it was steadily downhill from there, but that didn't matter as I enjoyed being part of a side which was promoted from Division 5 to Division 3 over a five-year period, contributing a hard-earned thousand runs in support of that upward trajectory.

So, as my cricket career spluttered on towards its fag end, my teaching at Frensham echoed a similar downward parabola. Apart from a small coterie of fans, my inability to keep up with the digital age and cope with the increasingly wide range of academic ability meant that I was viewed increasingly as a liability by children, parents and staff alike. There comes a moment when, as is said about all political careers, they end in failure. It was, however, within my grasp to define the termination of that failure and although, to parallel my cricketing ambition to score a ton, I wanted to notch up 100 terms in the classroom, in the end I expediently drew a close on my innings on 99 (very Bradmanesque in its acknowledgement of the need to keep immortality just out of reach).

Back to the old roots

What next? Well, in January 2013 I started a Critical/Creative Writing PhD at Chichester University on Anglophone Indian poetry. This was undertaken under the supervision of the poet and academic Stephanie Norgate and involved writing a collection of poems about my childhood in Calcutta alongside a study of Indian writers such as Amit Chaudhuri, Arun Kolatkar and Dom Moraes. A former pupil of Snezzy and me from Ardingly, Rohan Begani, had invited us to his lavish wedding in Bombay in 2010 and I had felt reconnected powerfully to the sub-continent where I spent my early formative years. I'd read voraciously since then about all things Indian and travelled the western seaboard of India – Goa and Kerala – and recently returned to that extraordinary city of extremes Calcutta accompanied by daughter Olivia. The PhD was completed in 2017 and led to the compilation of my collection 'Crow Dusk', published by the fine letterpress Paekakariki Press, about my childhood connections with India. I also joined the WEA tutor panel and taught courses on Anglophone Indian Literature, Psychogeography and Creative Writing.

On turning 60, I thought that my cricketing boots were finally due to be hung up for retirement. We sold our house in Hampshire and moved (mainly for financial reasons) to an obscure village called Black Torrington in rural north-west Devon. The intention was to pull up a chair by the fire with a tankard of ale in my hands and dream ancestral dreams until Alzheimer's erased me from any further responsibility for sentient life. However, as the blustery days of February gave way to March, the old juices reluctantly sprung into the cricketing limbs, and soon I was casting around websites for cricket clubs in rural Devon. Had not my cricket career started up on Devon soil? Should I not seek to put it to bed there? One final season ...!

The nearest club was at Hatherleigh, a charmingly authentic rural market town in the heart of Ruby Country. Like most of the region, the town blended a 1950s 'timewarp' atmosphere with an underlay of timeless agricultural cycles and pagan customs. The cricket club, however, was very much a going concern: it ran several successful sides in the Devon leagues, a burgeoning youth and women's cricket programmes, as well as boasting the best cream teas in the county. I decided that I would re-invent myself as a slow right-arm round-the-wicket bowler and see if the 3rd XI would give me an occasional outing. By 're-invention' I meant that I would try to con a fresh set of cricketers that I wasn't just a fagged-out old trundler but a bona-fide spinner playing out the golden sunset of my career! It's amazing how you can pull the wool over people's eyes (mainly because they're trying to do the same to you) if you stop to polish the ball, add a little scuffle and kick at the start of your run-up, contort your expression at point of delivery and then stare meaningfully down the pitch after you've released the ball. It helped that another

Mrs F, about to unleash a cricket tea at Hatherleigh

ex-schoolmastering spinner (a genuine leggie) on the verge of decrepitude was in the frame too. Together we hooked up as the 'spin twins' and like the famed West Indian duo, Ramadhin and Valentine, we decimated the local opposition with our pincer-like control from both ends – not hard when this was composed mainly of hungover, tractor-saddle-sore farm labourers prepared to take an uncouth swish at every ball. However, you take your gifthorses (not to mention war horses!) when and where you can and I was soon boasting an unprecedented (for me) brace of 'five fors'. Who needs to bat?

Early in May, one of the Hatherleigh CC 'vets' suffered a heart attack on the cricket pitch and nearly died. Luckily the ground he was playing on in Hampshire was equipped with a defibrillator, and he was resuscitated and rushed to nearby Portsmouth Hospital. He was captaining the Devon Over-60s in a County Seniors match at the time. Immediately I started to ruminate on the possibility of my following suit – not the coronary, but playing for the county. Now that I was 60, time was running out on my secretly nurtured ambition to play representative cricket. The irony was that I had to reach 60 to have a hope in hell of fulfilling such an ambition, yet the prospect of any meaningful longevity was fading by the day. Now or never – so I contacted Devon CCC, gave them my cricketing pedigree, brazened out my health record and waited to be rejected for my senescent hubris. One day in July, a phone call came through. I had been selected to play for the Devon Seniors 2nd XI against Worcestershire at home at Sandford CC.

I arrived at the ground like a nervous newboy. I was the first one there. Where could be found the limber athletes warming up in the nets, the stream of spectators at the turnstile gates? Soon a few cars rocked up, and some white-haired gents staggered towards the pavilion with their cricket 'coffins' in tow, followed by a gaggle of scorers, umpires and groupies (i.e. long-suffering partners). The match was to follow a 90-over format, and Devon were in the field first. I was interested to see what the standard would be like. Most of the Over-60s players are honest veteran club journeymen like me, though there is a smattering of cricketers who have previously played at representative level who find it hard to retire from the game completely. My observation of the ageing process in cricketers has been that the fielding goes first after about 40 years of age, the bowling loses its snap after 50 but that batting after 60, whilst lacking the sharpness of eye and dexterity of shot-making of youth, can still aspire towards a decent standard. My hunch proved right: the fielding was comically competitive and arthritic in equal measure, the bowling tidy and begrudging of scoring opportunities, but the batting was still fluent and often high-class. I didn't get a chance to bowl, and my fielding was (I thought) 'tiggerish', though a missfield I made off the opening bowler elicited a colourful tirade of expletives: old age takes no prisoners! When it was Devon's turn to bat I was due to come in at number seven but, alas or thankfully, my services weren't needed as the top order overhauled Worcestershire's score with ease.

Would I end up as a one-cap wonder who never batted or bowled for his county? A trip up to Gloucester to play Cheshire gave me my first bowling opportunity, and I conquered initial nerves to notch up a useful analysis of nine overs and one wicket for 36. This was followed by an overnight trip to Birmingham and Aston CC (home ground of Chris Woakes) to play Warwickshire which was less successful, and then the last game of the season against Wales at the South Devon CC in Newton Abbot gave me my moment of batting glory – a somewhat frenetic late-order 32 in a losing cause. Still, 32 against Wales … I'd take that back home to mull over in my coffin!

By the end of the season, the burden of playing for both Hatherleigh and Devon took its toll on my body. I developed chronic Achilles heel strain as well as fractured shins from my tendency to waft a leg at balls hit my way when fielding.

Was it time to pack in? Time would tell …

Time did tell … I spent the winter recovering from my ailments and started a programme of rehabilitation exercises in the gym at Okehampton. Future acts of glory (and folly) beckoned! I played some early-season indoor nets with Hatherleigh CC and then attended the Devon Over-60s' trial nets at Exeter University's school of sporting excellence. This was followed by trials at Bovey Tracey CC and selection for the 2nd XI squad. I hoped that I could consolidate on my sporadic performances of the year before and perhaps cement a steady berth. Then out of the blue came a summons to fill in for a late injury for the 1st XI against Hampshire up at the North Devon ground at Instow (stronghold of the legendary cricketer and umpire David Shepherd and nursery for the Overton twins). I was about to gain my O60s Seniors 1st XI county cap, so I was happy to turn up, put my body on the line at short leg, bowl into the gale of a wind and bat number eleven just to fulfil my sad little dream. As it turned out, I bowled badly into the wind, fielded atrociously and didn't get a bat, and was relieved to slip back to the seconds.

The months of May and June kept generally dry and I hit a good groove of batting for Hatherleigh. The Devon games were unremarkable except for a miserly bowling analysis return against Wales (cricket in Wales – another first ... "You need a fine leg there, boyo") of nine overs for fourteen runs. With my armoury of injury-preventative potions and unctions to hand, I seemed to be defying the inevitable injuries and a note of cocky hubris crept into my thinking as I outlined to myself an itinerary of games I intended to play. Fatal!

"Mark, are you free on Tuesday for the Firsts' game against Somerset?"

"Er, let me think, am I free? (of course I'm free – why this pretence of playing hard to get?) ... Yes, I think so, I'll just check with the wife ..."

"Great, 11 o'clock sharp at Hatherleigh. Be there."

Devon win the toss and put Somerset in. Their batsmen, snowy white of hair but fluent of stroke, carve us around the park. Eventually I get the nod. Nothing to lose. Eight overs later, 3-41 and clapped into the pavilion. Am I dreaming? (Do I still have dreams like this at 62 years of age? You bet.) After

Devon Seniors 2018

the break, Devon have a total of 223 to chase down. I'm in at number five, but I don't expect to bat. Suddenly two wickets are down, and I'm lounging about in the pavilion padless, gloveless, boxless, batless. Quick! Get ready! Just in time. A wicket falls, and I'm out there with the local Mr Cricket, Richard Tidball. A few respectable runs would do, occupy the crease for an over or two, do my bit. An hour later I'm still there, stroking the ball about and charging between the wickets like a gazelle (well ... stumbling down the track in an ungainly flurry of limbs and pads). The runs are accumulating, but I'm close to exhaustion. My partner calls for another quick single, and I launch myself in response. Next thing I'm soaring through the air before hitting the ground hard in a scramble of limbs, bat and pads. I can feel an ominous crack or two, and my body goes numb. I'm not sure how, but I get up and pretend all is fine ... it's not. I contrive to run myself out and get back to the pavilion. More claps – "38, mate, good knock ... Are you alright?" I'm in heaven (3-41, 38 runs and several broken ribs for my county).

Was it time to pack in? Time would tell ...

Winter brought its challenges. It rained and rained, and the dogs turned the house into a mudbath. I worked steadily on my sore Achilles heels with trips to the gym and long steady walks. However, just after Christmas, I faced a setback. Two of our dogs – our aged malcontent Jack Russell-cross Harry and the bumptious Alsatian Buddy – had a ferocious fight and I made the mistake of interposing my hand between their teeth in attempting to separate them. I received a nasty gash down my right forefinger and was rushed off to Casualty at the North Devon Hospital in Barnstaple. An overnight stay was required, followed by an operation performed under general anaesthetic early in the morning. I was desperate to leave hospital with an all-clear to fly to Jaipur the following week for the Jaipur Literature Festival. As it transpired, I was given the green light to travel, provided I accepted the risks of infection, so with hand bound up and a case full of dressings I set off to the land of the warrior Rajput. On return, my wound healed slowly and I developed a chest infection which left me gasping for air and passing out with worrying frequency. I couldn't see myself lining up for the next passage of play, let alone the start of the season, and postponed early-season nets by a month.

The April and May grounds were soggy, and I hit my first games like a geriatric sponge (what sort of a metaphor is that?). However, I opened the bowling for the O60s' Firsts at Bovey Tracey against Hampshire and claimed the scalp of one of the League's most prolific batsmen, Mike Swain, before travelling up to Worcestershire with the Seconds and sending down some rank long hops. The gloomy winter and a lack of net practice were telling. I needed my cricket muse to intervene: 'Could I revive within me her symphony and song/ To such a deep delight t'would win me/ That I would play that cover drive and topple those pesky bails ...' Luckily the weather started to warm up and, unbeknown to us, we were about to enter a three-month heat wave which would surpass the legendary glories of 1976. My batting for the Hatherleigh 3rds, coming in anywhere between six and nine, settled into a steady groove whilst with my bowling for Devon I began to eliminate the one horror ball per over and rack up some halfway decent analyses. Nevertheless, whilst Hatherleigh won every Saturday, Devon lost every Tuesday.

I have always lurked on the edge of masculine sporting groups. In any such cohort, there are the recognisable types: the cool Alpha male leader, his obsequious first lieutenant, the bully, the show-off, the team clown, the all-round 'good guy' and then me – the wall flower with a permanent cryptic smile pasted on to my face, good enough with bat and ball to have to be picked but the first one posted to short leg as cannon fodder. Despite all being in our sixties and depleted of 'cojones', the group types in the O60s dressing room were still very recognisable. Yet a mellowness (perhaps just a resignation before the inevitable onset of old age, dementia, you name it) tempered the hard surfaces of the 'types' and I tried to capture the bittersweet elegiac mood of the old cricketer's yearning to turn back the clock one last time in this poem:

OLD DEVON BOYS IN WHITE
Bandages are strapped on shoulders
and knees, linament rubbed
into rheumatic joints as the banter
bandies from played out jockstrap
tropes to gallow-humour jokes,
cricket boots bound to outlast
their hobbling owners' feet.

A toss of the coin and out they stumble –
eleven Old Devon Boys in white,
parking their stale marriages
fumbled pensions and broken dreams
to turn back the clock to when
cherub of cheek and limber of limb
they galloped to the crease
shirts flapping in the breeze
and hurled a red cherry
at three sticks in the ground.

93

Later they'll bathe in a haze of beer
reminisce over matches won and lost,
hearts de-fibrillating, fibs confabulating –
jostling for the next team sheet,
if selected, if
still standing.

Another obscure lifetime dream came true when I was asked to play for the Devon Dumplings against a touring side from Sydney. The President of the Dumplings is a Devon Senior player and had bumped into some availability hassles. I was more than happy to oblige. Ever since the father of my prep school friend Peter Randall-Johnson (from that talented Devon cricketing family) had arrived at the Fathers vs Sons game at St Michael's in 1968 kitted out in full Dumplings regalia, looking like a male version of the Queen of Sheba, I had aspired to count myself one of them. So, although I failed to acquire the outfit, I played and can have inscribed on my tombstone: 'Here lieth an ex-Dumpling'.

And so the season rolls to its close with England leading a series against India, the veterans Cook and Anderson approaching the swansongs of their careers (though both are not eligible to play real veteran cricket for another three decades – mere striplings!) and a nip of autumn can be smelt in the air. The Devon O60s approached their final hurdle. Having failed to qualify for the real play-offs and missed the Runner-up Plate play-offs through some skulduggery (dobbed in by a Worcestershire 'sneak' for playing an unregistered player), we faced the knock-out competition between the remaining eight counties for the Bowl. From the depths of a poor season we rose phoenix-like to the challenge of a quarter-final against Middlesex, followed by a triumphant semi-final against Leicestershire. After chucking down over 100 overs during the course of the season, my arm was well oiled and I put in some definitive spells of parsimonious old-man bowling. Suddenly we were in the final. Earlier in the summer Gareth Southgate's World Cup squad had come close to launching the country into the stratospheric euphoria reminiscent of 1966 revisited. We vowed to complete their unfinished business and make geriatric cricket the pride of the county! A Team Coach was commissioned by Devon CC, and we headed up to Chipping Sodbury to meet the mighty Bedfordshire in a clash of Titans (or at least titanium implants). We put them in first, and for once our batting flourished with Caribbean-style abandon and we posted a score of over 250: this took the pressure off our bowling. Fortunately, we didn't squander the advantage and had them five wickets down for 70-odd. The Bowl was as good as won, and we just had to administer the last rites before returning to the pavilion as winners. The jubilation was such that defibrillators were on hand to administer aid and the Air Ambulance put on alert in case of cardiac arrest – not a bad way to go!

Daughters Olivia and Natasha on a beach in Australia, blissfully unaware of the trials and tribulations of cricket obsession

Postscript

During the three years tinkering with this text, I have travelled from the age of 60 to 63 and show no signs of retiring to a life of reading my Wisdens by the fire. Inshallah, I shall take to the pitches again next spring and crank my body through some more contortions in pursuit of that elusive will-o'the-wisp of cricketing 'jouissance'. How long can I put off the inevitable? When does the parody of cricketing athleticism become so embarrassing that someone is consigned to straight-jacket you forcibly from further activity? Maybe never! And as I consider the joyful extension of cricketing life into the O70s, or the stunning example of local Hatherleigh vet Mick Massey, who at 86 continues to plonk the ball down on a sixpence, I reckon that I might just try to follow suit. That, if it occurs, may become the subject of a later memoir – entitled 'Zimmer Frame Glories', or some such. Meantime, another season peters out, the whites are washed and put on mothballs, the cricket coffin is zipped up.

Looking at my bat, I may just have to sneak up to Lillywhite's over the winter and purchase one final model.

That was never the deal.

The Accidental Shepherd

by
Gavin R. Dobson

CONTENTS

Clapham South

Geordie Kinloch and his colleague Robert Poovie walked out of the bank in Bishopsgate together and joined the evening tide of office workers flowing along Fenchurch Street towards Monument. Geordie was exhilarated by the sultry May weather, exclaiming,

'It's brilliant to see all these lovely girls in their short summer skirts.'

'Mmm... suppose so.'

Geordie didn't know Poovie well. He was considerably older and more senior than Geordie. He worked in Compliance, an arcane group of faceless back-office guys whose main function, as far as Geordie could tell, was to prevent new ideas being adopted at the bank. They both lived near Clapham Common and occasionally met on the way to or from work. This evening he was struck by how Poovie's eye was drawn more towards fashionable young men in expensive suits than the leggy objects of his own desire.

'I need to get the *Evening Standard* to see what's on.' Geordie announced as they approached the tube station.

Spotting the cluster of commuters around the newspaper vendor, Poovie suggested,

'Why don't you wait until we reach the other end? It looks like a real hassle here. Besides, there's something I'd like to discuss with you on the train.'

'No sweat. I'm sure the evening news can wait until I reach Clapham.'

In the Monument concourse the usual cluster of foreigners fumbled around the ticket machines. Maddening lines snaked back from the ticket booths, queuing to pay their fares. The barriers were, as usual, unmanned. Geordie put away his season ticket and Poovie fingered the coins in his pocket. The ticket queues provided his perennial excuse, should he ever be challenged, that he had been too pressed to wait for a ticket, and the money in his pocket was evidence that he had had every intention of paying the full fare.

They duly circumvented the queues, strode purposefully through the barriers and made their way underground to the Northern Line platform, heading south.

'I see you're a bit of a risk-taker.' Geordie observed.

'Not really. I just pay at the far end. It saves a huge amount of time over a year.'

'Why don't you just get a season ticket?'

'I'm on the road so much that it wouldn't be worth it.'

'Fair enough.'

'Yes, it is fare enough.' Poovie responded. The pun was lost on Geordie.

Robert Poovie's ploy had become so routine that he'd long lost the flutter of excitement as he approached the ticket barrier at his destination. His excuse, if ever one was required, was down pat, there would be a brief transaction with the ticket collector, he'd be allowed through the barrier and Bingo! Another £1.20 skimmed from the coffers of London Transport. Instead of paying the £4 fare from Monument to Clapham South, Poovie would always get away with paying the fare from a station nearer to Clapham South.

A wave of greasy stale air preceded the atrabilious clatter of the underground train as it swept into Monument station and decelerated along the length of the platform. The doors slid open, a metallic voice announced 'Mind the gap!' and the crowd surged into the carriages. Geordie and Poovie were lucky to find two empty seats together and sat down. Since Geordie had not bought the Evening Standard at the station, he was wondering how to sustain a conversation for the 20 minute ride to Clapham South when the older man pulled a letter out of his inner breast pocket.

'Here, read this.'

Geordie, flattered by the man's familiarity, took the letter.

Dear Robert,

Following our discussions the Chairman and Directors of

Cornfeldt Neustein are delighted to offer you the post of Assistant Director of Compliance, on the terms and conditions set out in the attachment that accompanies this letter.

We hope that you will be in a position to give us a favourable response at your earliest opportunity and we look forward to having you as a colleague at the Bank.

With best regards
Yours sincerely

Benjamin Feiertag,
Director of Compliance

'Wow. That's fantastic. Congratulations. Are you taking the job?'

'Well, what would you do?' Poovie handed Geordie the attachment with a blasé smile.

Geordie studied the sheet of paper. It offered a salary 120 per cent above current bank pay scales, six weeks holiday versus his current four, maximum pension contributions, first-class business travel, a substantial low-interest mortgage package, generous scholarships towards private schooling and so forth.

Geordie whistled.

'Well, I guess that answers the question, doesn't it? I assume that because you're telling me you've already decided to take the job and you've told your wife and everybody else?'

'No, you're the first person I've spoken to, but I have decided to take the job.' Then rather awkwardly, the older man added, 'And, er...I don't have a wife.'

'Well I appreciate your confidence in me. I won't tell anyone until it's a done deal. But congratulations in the meantime.'

'Thanks. Subject to the usual background checks and character references, I'll be joining Cornfeldt Neustein in a month.'

Poovie fell silent. He stared into middle space and exuded a warm satisfaction. Geordie studied him. He was in his forties, plump, thinning black hair greying at the temples, greasy skin. He was the

proverbial man in a crowd, cheaply but carefully dressed, utterly nondescript. He understood that after years of hard grind Poovie had finally transitioned from aspiration to success; he'd been recognized as a top talent by one of the top private banks in London.

He imagined that the familiar world of the Northern Line must already be feeling different to Poovie. He would now be a cut above the tired, malodorous South London passengers squeezed into this bloody metal tube day after day. Presumably he used to feel comradeship with his fellow commuters; they'd all slaved in the same mighty endeavour for years, pulling together for the City economy. But now he must be reflecting that his fellow passengers had never been true comrades, merely co-travellers out for themselves, just like him. Sometimes a lucky rat pulls ahead of the pack and never looks back. Geordie felt slightly envious of his colleague.

He wondered if Poovie would avail himself of Cornfeldt Neustein's mortgage facility to buy a magnificent pad in Chelsea. A car would pick him up in the morning and return him in the evening. It would be goodbye to the Northern Line. Or any line, for that matter. At worst, if the chauffeur was stretched, he might occasionally have to take the Circle or District Line from South Kensington straight up the embankment to Monument.

Geordie was too naïve, clearly, to guess that Poovie was dreaming of finding himself an Asian manservant, a sweet compliant Thai or maybe a Filipino. Yes, that would round off his life nicely. Poovie's heart leaped at the thought of it.

A student wearing faded jeans got on at Elephant & Castle and sat opposite them. He pulled a dog-eared paperback from a pocket in his knapsack, found his page and started reading. The book was *A Farewell to Arms* by Ernest Hemingway.

'*A Farewell to Alms*', Poovie observed to a bemused Geordie, who quite missed the pun. 'Ha Ha, how very apt. Life's about to take a radical turn for the better, no looking back.'

Six stations rattled past and the train slowed as it approached Clapham South. The two colleagues rose from their seats and made towards the exit with the thinning crowd. As they climbed the steps and emerged into the concourse, they saw the cordon of London Transport inspectors encircling the ticket barriers. The crowd shuffled forwards. Poovie turned to Geordie,

'You go ahead. I've got some errands to run. I'll see you in the office tomorrow.'

'All right,' Geordie replied and showed his season ticket to the avuncular West Indian inspector.

'Good evening and thank you sir.' The man said to him.

Geordie picked up an *Evening Standard* from a nearby vendor. He caught the headline and stopped in his tracks as he heard the words 'I got on at Oval.' He turned back to see Poovie hand £2.80 to the inspector. The West Indian replied courteously, 'I'm giving you one more opportunity, sir, to tell me where you got on.'

'I told you, I got on at Oval, and this is the correct fare.' Poovie looked indignant for being challenged.

'Very well, sir. I am obliged to take you in for further enquiries. Oval station has been closed all day today for emergency repairs.' The inspector nodded at two nearby London Transport police officers, who frogmarched the protesting Poovie to a van parked outside the station.

Geordie thought of running out to see what he could do to help, but was certain that Poovie would be mortified to know that his young colleague had witnessed his arrest, particularly after sharing that letter on the journey to Clapham South.

The following morning at 11 o'clock, an inter-office memo was circulated around the bank by the Director of Human Resources.

Yesterday evening a senior member of staff was apprehended by London Transport police for trying to evade paying a tube fare. Immediately after his arrest he admitted his stupidity and offered to pay full restitution. He was informed that he would be prosecuted for committing an offence under the Regulation of Railways Act 1889 and that a fine and a criminal record would be the likely consequence.

The Board considered the fact that he had been a valued member of staff for 17 years, but decided to terminate his employment on account of his inexcusable criminal behaviour. The Board would remind all bank employees that they are in a position of high fiduciary responsibility. Any behaviour by staff within or outside working hours which might compromise the bank's reputation for integrity will be dealt with summarily.

Geordie glanced at his colleagues on the trading floor. He'd known many shysters at the bank who'd got away with dubious, if not criminal, behaviour. It was usually because the markets had turned in the nick of time to cover their misdemeanours; sometimes it was because they were just too sophisticated to be detected. Yet. But poor bloody Poovie: an incredibly petty crime, some extraordinary bad luck and his career was blown out of the water. The Gods are simply against some people, Geordie reflected, as he recalled the headline in the prior day's *Evening Standard:*

FLOOD CLOSES OVAL STATION.

Rosselini's

Geordie discovered Rosselini's Shoeshine & Barber Shop while out for a stroll on a fine Saturday morning in May. He had been recommended many fashionable hair salons on the Near North side, but was always put off after an exploratory stroll past their windows. Most were too precious for his taste, if not downright threatening to his masculinity. He was not looking for a sensory experience, but a simple old-fashioned professional haircut at a reasonable price.

His first clip in Chicago had been at a hairdressing place near the Drake Hotel. Someone had said that Ronald Reagan got his hair done there when passing through town. Geordie, being of a sympathetic political persuasion, thought it might be fun to sport a presidential hairdo. A friend commented that his adulation was comparable to those European men in the 1930's who sported a toothbrush moustache in imitation of you-know-who. Well, the Reagan hairstyle didn't pan out. A prerequisite, of course, was RR's full head of hair, which Geordie's receding hairline could not match. The nicest compliment he received for his haircut was that it looked like he'd backed into a buzz-saw.

Rosselini's was on Dearborn, just round the corner from Hubbard. The window displayed a row of faded photographs of well-groomed matinee idols dating back to the 1940s. *'Here's a place that's comfortable with itself.'* thought Geordie, and pushed open the glass door.

A bell jangled on a spring as he entered. The parlour consisted of three large white ceramic basins on the right, up against a mirrored wall. Opposite each basin was a mechanical chair with worn chromed struts and levers to adjust their height and tilt. The seats and backs were of cracked red plastic, no doubt once as opulent as stuffed leather. At the rear of the room, glass shelves were lined with bottles of hair oil, racks of combs, hairbrushes, trade magazines and elderly copies of Reader's Digest. A high chair with a broad footrest was positioned at the end of a row of seats so that customers might get a shoe shine while they waited. Coils of fly paper hung limply in the window embrasure.

A middle-aged fellow in a white cotton barber's jacket was sitting in one of the chairs reading the Sun Times. He looked up.

'Er..I was wondering if I might have a haircut.'

'Sure, buddy, siddown.' He gestured to the neighbouring chair.

'Thank you. I want a light trim, off the ears, straight at the back, nothing fancy.'

'Sure thing.' He threw a blue sheet around Geordie's shoulders, stuffed a line of tissues around his neckline to prevent stray hairs from infiltrating his shirt and reached for a pair of scissors from the disinfecting jar.

'Been busy?' Geordie opened the conversation.

'Not today, but it was a full week. Where you from?'

'I'm British.' Geordie replied, anticipating the usual *'Gee, you've got such a cute accent, where you from?'* conversation.

'I think I guessed that,' The barber said nonchalantly, as if he'd read Geordie's conceit. 'Where from in Britain?'

'Scotland, originally.'

'Truth springs from argument among friends.'

'Sorry?'

'David Hume. A great Scotchman.'

'It's been a long time since I read anything by David Hume.' Geordie quickly covered himself, racking his memory in vain for anything intelligent to say about the philosopher.

'That's one of the problems in today's world.' The barber trimmed neatly around Geordie's right ear. 'This enough? It's just off the ear. I can take more off if you like.'

'No, that's perfect.'

'Generally speaking, the errors in religion are dangerous, those in philosophy only ridiculous.' The barber might have been discussing the weather as he went on to trim around Geordie's left ear. 'Yeah, if people read more Hume, there would be less stupidity and fundamentalism around. What drives me nuts is that all these matters were thought through 200 years ago, and people still address today's great issues as if they're uniquely today's problems.'

'That's an interesting point.' The guy was on a roll. Geordie let him continue.

'My name's Jim, Jim Rosselini.' He stood back to get a better perspective of his customer's head.

'Geordie Kinloch.'

'So whaddya do, Geordie?'

'Oh, I'm a financial type.' he replied cautiously.

'Mmm.' This was evidently a subject that Jim did not wish to pursue. After a pause he asked,

'So what's with this independence movement in Scotland?'

'Not my scene at all.' Geordie replied, 'But anyone can see that Scotland's voice is magnified hugely through Westminster. As a small independent socialist country, the debate will shift to fishing rights and nailing the few successful people dumb enough to stay behind.'

'The folks who lead the movement seem awful sure of themselves.'

'Yes they are, rather.'

'Where men are the most sure and arrogant they are commonly the most mistaken, and have given their reins to passion without that proper deliberation and suspense, which alone can secure them from the grossest absurdities.'

'Crikey, there's no answer to that.' Geordie was becoming mightily impressed by his coiffeur savant.

Jim reached for a mirror and showed Geordie his haircut.

'How's this?'

'A little more off the top, otherwise it's fine.' Geordie wanted to change the subject. He was in no mood for polemics on a warm Saturday morning. 'How long have you been here?'

'My father set up this barber shop in 1930 when he was 20 years old.' Jim replied proudly. 'He used to go round to the Tokyo Hotel and cut Al Capone's hair. Capone would have nobody else cut his hair, only my father.'

'That's impressive. Did your dad keep a diary? Did he talk about Al Capone? What was he like?'

'It was all before my time.' Jim side-stepped the question. 'See that chair over there?' He pointed at the high chair with a broad footrest.

'Yes.'

'Capone used to come here to get a shoe shine and a manicure. He sat on that chair while Willy polished his shoes and Nance polished his nails. The car waited outside; his guys stood round on the street, as far as the corner. Dad was always scared there would be another Valentine's Day massacre in his barber shop.'

'This actual barber shop?'

'Yeah, Al Capone came into this *actual* barber shop.' Jim mimicked his customer's British intonation.

'Amazing.' Geordie looked round. Sure enough, all the equipment and furnishings dated from the 1930s. He could see that little had changed. And Capone had sat in that very chair. Wow!

'What happened to your dad? Is he still alive?'

'He retired to Naperville, in the house he was born in. He's still alive but gettin' real forgetful.'

'Tell him there's a Brit who'd be interested to meet him.' He loved meeting people who'd had a brush with history. He'd had an old cab driver in Albany, New York recently. He'd been one of the few survivors of the sinking of *USS Indianapolis* in 1945, and another guy who'd flown Super Fortresses over Germany in 1945. He'd also met Memphis Slim in a bar in Ostend a long time ago, and once chatted to Koko Taylor at the Kingston Mines.

'Sure, I'll tell him.' Jim gave the final touches to Geordie's haircut and whipped the blue sheet off him with the flourish of a toreador. 'Will that be all, sir?'

Geordie caught himself in the mirror. Jim had given him exactly the right trim. 'For today, yes. But I'll be back in a week or two.'

He paid the barber the small amount requested and gave a substantial tip. He wondered how the fellow managed to keep a business going, pay his rent, his exorbitant city taxes and stay alive on the odd passer-by dropping in for a haircut. He was half way out of the door when he paused and turned around,

'As a matter of interest, what if I'd said I was German when I came in the door?'

Jim was settling back in his chair with the *Sun Times*. He looked over his spectacles at Geordie. 'A subject for a great poet would be God's boredom after the seventh day of creation.'

'Sorry?'

'Nietzsche, my man. We'd have talked Nietzsche.'

Amarillo Nights

The family had just sat down for dinner, chattering happily as they anticipated the steaming array of vegetables, roast chicken and all the fixings laid out on the kitchen table.

'Please everyone -help yourselves.' Josie insisted. Serving dishes were passed around. Sweet corn, new potatoes, carrots and chicken were scooped hungrily onto waiting plates.

'This is quite delicious, darling.' Geordie complimented his wife. He was positioned at his usual spot at the head of the table. To his left sat their son William, aged 17, and a college friend, Stephen. To his right sat their daughter Emily, aged 14, and a school friend, Erica. Josie sat opposite him. After William had poured a decent-looking bottle of Australian chardonnay into the waiting glasses, he toasted his mother.

'Cheers, Mum! Thanks for a great spread.'

The family tucked in. The agreeable clatter of cutlery on plates and the banter of a family dinner resonated through the house. Emily and her friend talked of mucking out the stables and grooming horses that afternoon, for which William teased them.

'I've never understood the attraction of horses. They're such a fag to maintain.'

'You don't understand.' Emily riposted.

'What's to understand about shovelling manure out of a shed?'

Emily caught Erica's eye and they erupted in giggles.

The rear door-bell rang.

'Who could it be at this hour?' Josie was irritated to be disturbed at dinner time.

'Oh, it's probably something to do with the farm.' Geordie replied. 'I'll go — just carry on with the meal, I'll be back in a minute.' He left the table and headed along the passage to the rear of the house, wiping his mouth with a napkin as he went.

A youth stood on the doorstep. He was tall, blond and athletic, dressed in well-cut jeans, cowboy boots and a red Dallas Cowboys fleece. He looked about the same age as William, in his late teens. There was something familiar about his open face and shy smile. Geordie naturally assumed he must be a school friend of William. A pretty girl of about the same age sat in a rented Peugeot parked in the courtyard. She watched him intently.

'Hello, can I help you?' Geordie asked breezily.

'I dunno, sir, but I'm lookin' for Mr Geordie Kinloch.' He spoke in a soft Southern accent.

'That's me.' Geordie was surprised the visitor hadn't asked directly for William.

The boy looked strangely at the older man framed in the doorway. Geordie wore a scruffy pair of brown corduroys, worn brown brogues, a frayed Viyella shirt and a torn green sweater. Farm wear. On the face of it, the two could not have been culturally more distant.

'Well sir, I have reason to believe you may be my father.'

Geordie laughed. Nice one. He vowed to get William back for this practical joke. The American boy was not put off by Geordie's reaction, however. He continued,

'You met my mother on a flight from Chicago to Dallas. She was living in Amarillo at the time and you were living in Chicago.'

A thunderbolt hit Geordie in the chest. He was stunned.

'My twin sister and I were born nine months later.' The boy gestured in the direction of the Peugeot. Geordie looked up at the girl in the car. She gave him a cheery wave. He smiled thinly.

'Her name is Roseanne, and my name is Johnny.'

'Roseanne and Johnny.' Geordie repeated quietly.

'Yes, sir.'

'How long are you here for, in Scotland? '

'We arrived this morning and we are planning to spend one week in Scotland, sir.'

'You ... will understand that this is a bit unexpected. I don't know what to say.'

Johnny looked puzzled. 'You didn't know about us?'

'No, I didn't know about you.' Geordie replied quietly.

Johnny lowered his eyes towards his finely tooled Texas boots.

Geordie was dumbfounded. That adage about life flashing before his eyes ... He had a handful of seconds in which to react sensibly or his world would cave in.

'Er, I think we need to talk, but right now I have guests here. Can I suggest that we meet tomorrow morning?'

Johnny nodded.

'Go to the Earl's Arms Hotel in the village. Tell the proprietor, Mrs McKay, that I sent you. I'll call and tell her that I will pay for your accommodation. Can you meet me there for breakfast?' He knew that whatever these kids might tell Doris McKay, she would be extremely discreet. She'd witnessed the full gamut of country weekend shenanigans over the years and totally understood the omerta that attaches to being a successful innkeeper.

'Yes, sir.' Johnny offered his hand. Geordie liked his straight eye and firm handshake. He looked over the boy's shoulder at Roseanne in the car. Her brow furrowed as she figured that the meeting was over.

'I will see you at 8 o'clock tomorrow morning for breakfast at the inn.'

Geordie stood on the doorstep with his arms crossed as the boy returned to the car. When he was certain they'd driven away down the drive, he closed the door quietly and walked along the corridor back to the kitchen.

'What was that all about, Dad?' Emily enquired as he returned to the dinner table. The meal had progressed. They were putting the finishing touches to a dish of strawberry and rhubarb pie; the dogs were circling for their share of the pre-wash routine.

'Oh, just farm business. It seems that there may be a problem with wild oats,' he said seriously, hoping that nobody would ask him to elaborate. Nobody did. 'I'll have to deal with it first thing in the morning.'

14

After dinner Geordie slipped outside with the dogs. A hundred yards from the house he stopped under a tree, unwrapped a King Edward from its transparent film, struck a match and puffed on the cheap cigar until the tip glowed. He hadn't smoked for ages. In the old days, he'd go for a brisk walk with a Havana after dinner to steady his nerves when he was embroiled in business deals. It helped him think straight and calm down before turning in for the night.

'Well, well, well. How do I explain this one to Josie and the family?' He addressed the trees as he ambled along, exuding a thin cloud of blue smoke. The dogs ferreted about in the undergrowth. They were wonderful companions, a great solace and mercifully incapable of comprehending the appalling guile of their master.

By the time King Edward had diminished from five inches to two and Geordie had paced about two miles of farm track, he was full of resolve.

'*Tell the truth, mate. You won't have to lie and actually it's not that serious',* he tried to convince himself as the dogs looked up and cocked their heads quizzically. 'But not until I've heard what those kids have to say at breakfast in the morning.'

He looked differently towards his family as they sat before the television, announcing, 'I'm heading off to bed. I've got to get up early.'

Josie looked up momentarily from the TV. 'You look like you've seen a ghost.'

'I'm just tired. See you when you come up after your movie.'

He stripped and climbed into bed where he lay staring at the ceiling unblinkingly for the best part of an hour.

Geordie parked the Land Rover in an inconspicuous space in a side street and walked the hundred yards to the Earl's Arms. He almost knocked over Doris McKay as he entered the lobby. She was carrying a tray of dirty dishes towards the kitchen, a dishcloth draped over her arm.

'Ah, good morning, Doris. Did you get my message?'

'Aye, Geordie. Your guests are in the dining room.' she replied matter-of-factly. Either she was an amazing poker player, Geordie thought, or she knew nothing. He assumed the latter; there was not even a twinkle of mischief in her eye as she bustled with her tray towards the kitchen.

The twins were sitting at an oval table recessed into a window alcove in the dining room. Its pristine cloth was set for three. In the centre was the normal paraphernalia of a B&B breakfast: a marmalade pot, salt & pepper shakers, a butter dish, a bowl containing wrapped sugar portions and a cheap vase containing a bouquet of fake roses. The twins were positioned at opposite ends of the table, leaving ample space for Geordie to take his place between them.

'Well, good morning Johnny.' He shook the boy's hand 'And good morning, Roseanne.' he gripped hers. 'We didn't meet properly last night.'

Four eyes drilled into him, not unpleasantly, but with frightening intensity. They were the thirsty eyes of desert travellers who had finally found their oasis. They drank in everything about him. His hair, greying at the sideburns and thinning on top, his hands coarsened by farm work, his tailored but well-worn tweed jacket. For his part Geordie was struck by their wholesomeness: nice-looking kids, tall, slim, pure complexions, neatly dressed. Roseanne was a young Grace Kelly; Johnny was clean-cut and taciturn. William and Emily, his "real" children, were also good-looking, but had developed the louche scruffiness, cynicism and understatement of British teenagers that distinguished them from their American counterparts.

'Tell me about your mother,' Geordie began. In the old days he might have wormed his way out of a situation like this by strenuous denials and alibis. But today, DNA testing rendered such lies obsolete. Besides, the kids were so obviously his. Why would he want to hurt them?

'She's fine, sir.'

'Does she know you're here?'

'Yes sir. She said that when we were 18 we could come and find you. We saved and told her we would come and look for you as soon as we could.'

'Well, that's nice,' Geordie replied unconvincingly. 'What did you expect?'

'We just wanted to meet our father.' Roseanne said disarmingly, looking down at her hands.

'I was under the impression that you had a father in Texas. I was brought in, er, as it were, to…er…'

'Fertilize Mom's eggs.' Johnny cut to the chase.

'Yes, that's right, yes, fertilize Mom's eggs.' Geordie was startled by the candour of the boy.

'We love her deeply, but she deceived you, sir.' Johnny began, 'She said she sat beside you on American Airlines flight 2333 from Chicago to Dallas one October day eighteen years ago and you got talking to each other. She decided there and then that she wanted you to be the father of her children.'

'She told me she was happily married. I certainly told her I was not looking for that kind of commitment.'

'She set you up with a story, sir. That's what she told us.'

'She told me she was married and couldn't conceive by her husband—whom she loved very much—and asked me to be her, er …'

'Sperm donor.' Roseanne filled in for his bashfulness. Her eyes bored into him.

'Well, yes. I'm truly delighted to meet you, but she swore the whole process would be entirely anonymous and there would never be any repercussions or consequences for me. Now here we are sitting 18 years later, having this awkward conversation.'

'Did you love our mother?' Roseanne asked.

'I barely knew her. She was an attractive lady, I remember, but I only ever spent a few hours with her. It was set up like a business transaction, with the full knowledge of her husband, she assured me.'

'Mom spoke very fondly of you as we grew up. You were the magical person from Scotland. We were just brought up to believe that daddies were like that—remote and loving, but invisible.'

'Remote and loving but invisible...' Geordie repeated vaguely, wondering why their mother had needed to mention him at all. Why hadn't she and her husband simply accepted her impregnation as their own and shut up? Doris McKay placed a cafetiere on the table. Geordie slid it towards Roseanne. 'Here, you plunge it. Show me what my daughter's made of,' he said sweetly. She plunged it carefully and looked business-like as she filled the coffee cups.

'Well, you'll understand that I have a dilemma. I'm not going to deny a liaison with your mother. That would be incredibly hurtful and disloyal to you. I mean, Johnny, you look too much like me at your age. I couldn't dodge this bullet even if I wanted to, and I won't. I just need to think about how to present this predicament to my family here.' He opened his arms towards the pair and laughed nervously.

'Sir, we didn't come to get anything from you, or cause you any embarrassment.' Johnny put his hand on Geordie's shoulder in a filial gesture.

'We simply wanted to understand our roots in Scotland.' Roseanne added, 'And Mom never had a husband. She always talked of you as being too tough an act to follow, so she never married anyone else.'

'Too tough an act to follow? Good Lord.' He had known her for less than 24 hours. How could she possibly have brought up her kids, saying that?

'Yes sir, that's what she has always said to us.' Johnny said.

'Let's change the subject. Why don't you tell me about yourselves? I want to hear everything about you—where you were born, your school, your interests, your friends, your ambitions.'

The following two hours were spent in a cultural tour de force about growing up in Amarillo, Texas. Roseanne had been a cheerleader at Amarillo High School, Johnny an athlete. Now,

Roseanne was headed to design school in Austin and Johnny to study veterinary medicine at Texas A&M.

For his part, Geordie gave them a précis of his life, his parents— the twins' paternal grandparents, for heaven's sake—his career, life on a Scottish farm and how he had ended up on that fateful flight from Chicago to Dallas. He told them they had two younger step-siblings and felt certain they would all get on well together.

Geordie looked at his watch. 'Well my friends, it's past ten o'clock and I need to get on. I have a meeting with our farm manager,' he lied. Then in a remarkably stupid burst of bonhomie, he added, 'Can I suggest that you both come over to Balnadarg at 6 o'clock to meet the family? I'll speak to Josie beforehand and everything will be squared off.'

'That would be very nice,' Roseanne looked at her brother, nodding her head enthusiastically.

'Good, why don't you give me your mobile number so I can call if there's a glitch.'

He wrote the twins' number on a paper napkin, shook their hands and rose from the table. He drove home as fast as the narrow lanes permitted. He had a few things to discuss with his wife.

Emily and Erica were in the kitchen when he returned.

'Where's Mum?' he asked.

'She's out for the day, doing her rounds. She left a short while ago and said she wouldn't be back until late afternoon.'

'Where will she be?'

'Dunno, Dad. She just said she had a lot to do and wouldn't be back till late afternoon.'

'Oh gawd! I'll have to find her.'

Geordie spent the next two hours trying to track down his wife, leaving increasingly desperate messages for her to return his calls. They lived in a rural area where there were many black-spots without mobile reception. Normally Geordie welcomed the lack of a signal; he enjoyed being inaccessible. He often derided his kids for being on the phone all the time, blustering at them with comments like 'In my day we had to write letters'. Now he was well and truly hoisted by his own petard, steadily feeling the noose tightening and his life ebbing away.

He changed tack and tried phoning the twins on the number they'd given him. Naturally, he encountered the same problem. They were probably driving around the Highlands admiring the scenery. He needed to put off their visit until later in the week, but there was no reception, no means of conveying a message to them.

He drove back to the Earl's Arms to leave a written message. Doris McKay said they'd told her they wouldn't be back until 'much later'.

By 2 o'clock it was clear that he'd temporarily exhausted his options, so Geordie drove back home. In a state of mounting agitation he took another elderly King Edward from its packet and strolled to a clearing in the woods. He ignited the cigar and lay on the grass, staring at the innocent white clouds scudding past the tree tops.

'How the hell did I get into this pickle?' he asked out loud.

He had long since dismissed, practically forgotten, the episode in Texas and hadn't given it any further thought for years. It had all started on an American Airlines flight—AA2333, he had been reminded at breakfast—from O'Hare to Dallas, eighteen years earlier. He tried to recall the details of his encounter.

Everyone had boarded, the flight crew were preparing to close the doors, Geordie was comfortably installed in an aisle seat and it looked like his adjacent window seat would be one of the few unoccupied seats on the aircraft. He lifted the arm rest and was spreading his papers over the spare seat when there was a tremendous flurry at the door. An attractive, if harassed, young woman carrying an arm load of shopping and boxes came tottering precariously down the aisle and stopped beside him:

'That's my place,' she announced breathlessly, pointing at the empty seat beside Geordie.

'Oh, I'll make space.' He cleared his papers, unbuckled his seat belt and stood up to help her stow the boxes in the overhead compartments. Once everything was distributed she slumped into the window seat. Fanning herself with a copy of Vogue she turned to Geordie, 'You're a real gennleman to help me like this. It's been a crazy morning.'

'Not at all. It's a pleasure to help you.'

'Holy Moses! Where is that accent from?' she turned round to face him directly.

'Oh, I'm British.' She was an attractive woman in her late twenties, with laughing green eyes, high cheekbones, tanned complexion and thick blonde hair. She wore a light silk blouse and a well-cut beige linen suit that outlined a startling figure. Geordie twiddled nervously with his signet ring. She wore a sapphire ring mounted ostentatiously with a cluster of yellow diamonds, coupled with a nugget of a ring on her wedding finger. The boundaries were clear for all to see.

'Briddish? How very cute. What are you doing in America?'

The conversation panned out with remarkable openness, particularly after the flight had reached cruising altitude and the pair had worked their way through three Johnny Walkers apiece. They gabbled like old friends. When they spilled out of the gate into the concourse in Dallas they found a quiet spot in the corner of a bar and continued their acquaintance.

'I feel like I've known you all my life,' she announced.' But don't get me wrong. I love my husband.'

'And I respect that'. Geordie responded with all the hopelessness of King Canute failing to hold back the North Sea.

'It boils down to this, Honey.' She massaged his thigh.' My George is an older man. Viagra makes him potent, but it hasn't made him fertile. We've been looking at fertility treatments for two years. You know how it works? You choose if you want an athlete or a physicist. Then you choose black, white or Cherokee, whatever you want. The clinic sources the appropriate test tube and they inseminate you.'

'But so far, no joy?' Geordie had had no direct experience of this

procedure as it related to humans, but knew all about artificial insemination. He'd grown up on a cattle farm.

'No Darlin'. No joy, either in the process or in the result,' she sighed. Her hand wandered suggestively around his nether regions, to the point where Geordie was in no doubt as to where this evening was leading. 'I see no reason to carry on goin' to the clinic when I've found a man who will provide all the genes a gal could want.' She kissed his neck.

'I ... suppose I could provide the service,' Geordie acquiesced, 'but that's where it would have to end.'

'George would never know. He'll think I got pregnant at the clinic and he'd be the daddy.'

'And you would never see me again?'

'No sir. That would be that.' She pouted, 'Unless ...'

'No unlesses.' Geordie said firmly through a cloud of whisky.

'Just one night.'

'Just one night. And pray God it works.'

'And I'd never know the result?'

'You'll never know the result. It will be between George and me.'

The encounter turned out to be decidedly more athletic than clinical. As they collapsed afterwards on the king-size bed, she whispered, 'I needed a ho-listic experience to get pregnant, not just a test tube'. She left very early to catch her commuter flight to Amarillo. Geordie slept on for two hours and completed his business around Dallas and Fort Worth over the following days.

He had not asked her name. He knew that her husband was called George, that she lived in Amarillo, was sassy and beautiful, well-travelled and shared a surprisingly wide range of interests with him. He had not told her his name either, although he reckoned she'd probably taken one of the calling cards that he'd scattered with other papers on the credenza in the hotel room after checking in.

The incident was a few months before he'd met Josie and he'd given it virtually no further thought over the years. It had occurred during a period of intense personal and professional activity; the memory of it had sunk beneath the waves of a very busy life. He did occasionally dream about undefined secrets lurking in his life, but always woke up before any secret was revealed. And Josie was always there beside him when he woke up.

The fire in King Edward had gone out. Geordie flicked the stump of the tired cigar into the damp grass and headed home. It was 3.45pm and he should be able to get hold of Josie or preferably, the twins, to put them off coming round at six that evening.

Both phones were still evidently in black spots and not receiving messages. He tried the Earl's Arms again. No twins. He began to panic. He had to head them off before they showed up at six o'clock. Or steer Josie first into a corner to explain. Preferably both. His encounter in Dallas had been entirely for philanthropic reasons, to help a childless family in need. Josie would understand, wouldn't she?

At twenty minutes to six, Josie's car rolled up. Geordie rushed into the courtyard to greet her. 'Hi. How was your day? I've been trying to get hold of you. We really need to talk.' he began as she opened the car door.

'Look, Geordie, not right now. I've had a heck of a day. I need to make an urgent phone call. Why don't you pour me a drink and we can talk afterwards?'

'How long will your call be?'

'Fifteen, twenty minutes. Not more.' She bustled past him, disappearing down the corridor to her office.

'Champagne? Such a treat,' Josie exclaimed delightedly. She took a long, slow draught and curled up on the sofa. 'So what was it that you needed to talk about so urgently, Honey?'

'Well, there's something we need to discuss....' he began.

The doorbell rang.

Still Short and Waiting

'"The game of speculation is the most uniformly fascinating game in the world. But it is not a game for the stupid, the mentally lazy, the man of inferior emotional balance, or for the get rich quick adventurer. They will die poor." '

Jake Birnbaum quoted these lines and looked Geordie in the eye.

'Jesse Livermore has always been the strongest influence on my investing style.'

'Why's that?' questioned Geordie.

'Because he set a strategy and let it run. He had a clear view of the market and placed enormous bets behind his views.'

'He was famous for being bearish, wasn't he? He always expected the market to fall.'

'Dead right. He felt—as I feel now—that great fortunes are to be made by selling stocks short. He sold stocks he didn't own, then bought them back once the price had fallen, and pocketed the difference.'

'IF he was right. Was he ever long in the stock market? Did he ever invest on the assumption that markets would go up?'

'Oh, I'm sure he did, but he was most famous for shorting crashes, like the crash of 1907 and the big one in 1929. He reputedly made $100 million by shorting the 1929 crash. That is equivalent to billions today.'

'In other words he sold a mass of stocks before the crash of '29 and bought them back after they'd fallen.'

'Correct. Ever since I read his book—Reminiscences of a Stock Operator—I have invested on the short side of the market.'

'Even in a bull market, when stocks are rising?'

'Particularly in a bull market. There are always sectors or sub-sectors going down when the general market is going up. There's always a stock whose price has got ahead of itself and is ready for a sell-off.''

'Doesn't it require a lot of energy if you always have to go short? After all, there are times when markets are going up strongly and you should just go with the flow. Wasn't it Jesse Livermore who said "There's only one side of the market and it's not the bull side or the bear side, but the right side"?'

'I can't argue with that.'

'So why don't you go long in bull markets, when stocks are going up, and short in bear markets, when stocks are going down? Isn't that the best strategy?'

'Not if your strategy is to be short.' Jake was a stubborn man, Geordie reflected.

'Fair enough, but it's late June and the market is up 8 per cent so far this year. Being short in the market since January must have been ruinous.' Geordie observed.

'So far, yes. But, don't you remember all the New Year forecasts that came out in the press? Last December every economist, all the major financial columnists, the TV commentators, all of them were uniformly optimistic for this year. I can't recall a single dissenting voice.'

'So?'

'So, if everyone is so optimistic it makes sense to take the opposite view. All that optimism is already reflected in share prices. Everyone was talking their own book because they were already invested in the market.'

'But they were right, weren't they?'

'So far, yes. But the market is struggling to move forward now. The firepower is spent, buying breadth is fading, trading volume is light when the market rises and heavy on days when the market falls. That's a sure sign of a market that's about to fall.'

'How so?'

'When upside volume is light, it means there's no buying conviction in the overall market. People are not rushing to follow the trend. On the other hand, heavy volume on the downside means than people are jittery. Any sign of a downside break in the market and you'll get huge volume days. The mood can easily turn to panic as people get out of the market to protect their wealth.'

'Fear overtakes greed in the market.'

'Correct. I am anticipating a non-linear market dislocation.' The unsmiling Jake liked to throw out delicious pieces of jargon.

'You're what?'

'A crash, Geordie. A crash.'

'Mmm, a non-linear market dislocation. I'll have to remember that.' Geordie paused as Jake's eyes darted before his screen. He had the jitteriness of all traders. 'So how are you playing the market's imminent downturn?' Geordie enquired.

'There are many ways. You can short the stocks of companies like Apple, Ford, IBM, JP Morgan, companies like that.'

'But to do that successfully you've really got to know your company and all the dynamics behind the current share price.' Geordie pointed out.

'Yeah, that's right ...'Jake replied vaguely as he tapped out some keys on his Bloomberg. 'Just a moment Geordie, I gotta concentrate here for a few minutes.' This was followed by an orgy of typing, clacking and grimacing as Jake got up to speed on today's market. 'Damn —the market's goin' up.'

'Most people celebrate when the market goes up.'

'Yeah, but not if you're positioned like me. I'm not only short, I'm triple short.'

'Triple short? What does that mean?'

'It means that if the market goes down 1 per cent, I go up 3 per cent.'

'And if the market rises 1 per cent?'

'You got it. I go down 3 per cent.' Jake said absent-mindedly as he scrutinized his screen for the faintest, hopeful sign of a market crash. After a few minutes he spoke to Geordie again. His brow was furrowed and he looked pale.

'Yeah, market today's up across the board. I simply don't understand what's goin' on. Banks are bust, government's bust,

Europe's bust, oil's rising, inflation's rising, Middle East in flames, tension ripping the West, Iran blocking Hormuz, Argentina pissing at the Falklands, 25 per cent unemployment in Spain, Chinese real estate rolling over and crash ...'

'But the market's going up.'

'Yeah, but not for long. Stock market's gonna crash, it's a house of cards.'

'So, we're about to experience a non-linear market dislocation?'

'Yeah, couldn't put it better myself.' Jake failed to detect the irony in Geordie's words as he scanned the screen.

'You could argue that stock markets are a huge discounting mechanism. Everyone knows about the problems you talk about, but perhaps the markets are looking through today's troubles to a brighter future beyond. They have already discounted all the bad news.' Geordie was forever Mr Glass-half-full.

'You always get a climactic sell-off before markets can rise again. We need a 30 per cent drop in valuations before we can have a healthy bull market here.'

'Maybe, but 30 per cent from what level? Markets might have their climactic selloff from a level 50 per cent higher than they are today. Why don't you go long the market today with enough hedges in place to protect your downside, run it for a while, then go short? That way you'll benefit from the market's rise and have more capital to short the market when—or if—your climactic selloff happens.'

'You gotta have a high pain threshold in this business. If I sold my shorts today and the market fell tomorrow I'd have zero cred left. You gotta suffer for your convictions.'

'Religious convictions, yes. Financial convictions, no.'

'I'll just have to tough it out in this market.'

'Didn't Livermore say, "The market can remain irrational longer than you can stay solvent." '

'No, actually that was Keynes.' Jake replied humourlessly.

Jake and Geordie had been good friends for many years. Geordie's harsh commentary was never taken the wrong way, and nor was Jake's when the boot was on the other foot.

'You mentioned that shorting individual stocks was one way to play the short side of the market.' Geordie began again. 'What other ways of shorting do you use?'

'Actually, I rarely short individual stocks. I tend to short the entire market based on macroeconomic observations. As I've said, the outlook is so dire at the moment that shorting the entire market's the only smart thing to do. It's a slam dunk.'

'....that's not working.'

'Yet, Geordie, yet. Look man, it's a long-term play.' Jake was becoming exasperated with his friend.

'So how do you implement your strategy? How do you go about shorting the entire market?'

'At the moment, I'm buying ETFs.'

'ETFs? '

'Yeah, Exchange Traded Funds. They're listed on the New York Stock Exchange and have a clearly-defined objective. You can get ETFs specializing in emerging markets, the airline industry, the mining sector, oil & gas and almost any sector you care to mention. Most sectors have ETFs that are long and the manager generally offers a shadow ETF that's short the sector.'

'So if you think the outlook is good for oil & gas, you can buy an ETF that invests only in oil and gas'.

'Correct. And if you think the ass will fall out of oil & gas, you buy the short ETF.'

'So, ditto with the whole market?'

'Sort of—you choose which index you want to short. You can short the S&P500, the Russell 2000 or virtually any industrial sector represented in these indexes. You can also go long these indexes if that's your gig.''

'You have such enormous choice,' Geordie remarked, 'How did you decide which index to short right now?'

'I'm short the Russell 2000. It's an index of smaller companies. When the market rolls over, smaller companies lead the way down.

Small companies are more volatile on the downside.'
'And on the upside.' Geordie pointed out.
Jake grimaced.
'Yeah. The Russell's up 8 per cent year to date. I'm triple leveraged on the downside, which means my portfolio is down 24 per cent.'
'How long have you held this, er, triple short ETF?'
'Five months.'
Geordie whistled. 'You must have patient clients.'
'Yeah, but they understand exactly where I'm coming from. My clients pay me to take the short side of the market. They have other managers who invest on the long side. ' Jake replied vaguely. He added without much conviction, 'They're cool with what I'm doing for them.'
Geordie figured that Jake's clients would be anything but cool. He certainly wouldn't be cool if someone lost him 24 per cent of his wealth, that's for certain.
'Well, when the market eventually cracks you'll be in the right place.'
'For sure.' Jake permitted himself the ghost of a smile, followed immediately by a frown. His patience suddenly cracked as he witnessed the morning's upsurge in equity markets on his Bloomberg screen.
'Look man, I gotta get on. Here, take this.' He handed Geordie a Summary Prospectus of a triple-leveraged ETF designed to short the Russell 2000 index. With a determined smile, he summed up his current investment philosophy, 'Yeah, I'm still short and waiting.'
Geordie rolled up the prospectus and slid it into his coat pocket, said his farewells and left Jake's office. He took an elevator down to the airy glass-covered lobby of the building and walked across its chequered marble floor to the Florentine Espresso Bar at the far end. Its customers were sharply-dressed young financial types queuing for their mid- morning shots of latte in ribbed takeaway cups.
He sat at a table sipping his decaffeinated double espresso—a

beverage as effective as a neutered stud horse, Jake had once observed caustically—and pulled out Jake's prospectus. It was a perfect example of the sort of toxic product designed to make money for its managers and carry the potential to destroy wealth for its customers. No doubt following a blizzard of customer complaints, the prospectus highlighted its risks explicitly.

'The Fund seeks daily leveraged investment results and does not seek to achieve its objective over a time scale of longer than one day.'

Indeed, the risks were so clearly spelled out that a reader might think that the managers were protesting too much, therefore the risks had to be exaggerated, therefore it must be a great investment.

'This Fund is recommended solely for sophisticated investors acquainted with the consequences of seeking daily leveraged investment returns, who have a clear understanding of the risks of shorting and leverage.'

'Blimey.' Thought Geordie, 'Everyone likes to consider himself a sophisticated investor. What a hook.'

'The pursuit of such leveraged investing means that Fund results for periods of longer than one day may bear no resemblance to longer term index return. This is because the aggregate return of the Fund is the product of multiple daily leveraged returns for each trading day.'

Geordie finished his coffee. He had an uneasy feeling that Jake had misunderstood what he'd invested in. Jake's view of the market's imminent demise might or might not prove correct, but this Fund was the wrong way to execute that hunch. The daily decay of assets meant that there would be little left to play with when Jake's prediction came right.

Thirty minutes remained before Geordie's next meeting. He decided to return to Jake's office for a few minutes to voice his concerns. As he ascended the tower in the elevator he recalled another of Livermore's sayings. It was something like, 'You can do all the right things at the right time, and be one hundred per cent wrong.'

There was commotion at the reception desk when he arrived at Jake's office. Three girls were in tears, the receptionist was distraught. Guys in suits were making their way briskly down the corridor; they entered the men's room and came out almost immediately, looking pale and shocked. They huddled and spoke in low tones in the corridor.

'Hi..er, I've come to see Jake again.' Geordie announced to the receptionist.

'Mr Birnbaum is not available.' She told him.

'Oh, I was with him just half an hour ago. He gave me this.' Geordie flourished the prospectus. 'I'd like to discuss it with him for a few minutes.'

'Are you a relative of Mr Birnbaum's?'

'No, just a friend.'

'Well sir, I repeat that Mr Birnbaum is not available.'

'Fair enough. In that case would you just tell him that Geordie Kinloch dropped by, and will call him later?'

'I don't think that will be possible, Mr Kinloch.' She said tearfully.

As he exited into the atrium below, a 3-man paramedic team brushed past him into the elevator, wheeling an empty emergency stretcher.

Geordie could get no reply from Jake or his office for the rest of the day.

It turned out that Jake had emulated his hero to the end. In 1940 Jesse Livermore blew his brains out in the Sherry Netherland. Jake's location was also on 5th Avenue, but a little further south.

Claret for Life

Desmond Thomson was another of those entrepreneurial rogues who had taught the young Geordie Kinloch much of what he knew about finance and a few other things besides. He was a square, craggy, blue-eyed Scot with unkempt grey hair swept back in the manner of an Old Testament prophet. Desmond Thomson was the global financier who commanded centre stage and Geordie Kinloch the bag-carrier who made it all happen.

Once, after a long day on the road they arrived at the Hyatt Regency Embarcadero in San Francisco. They checked in, picked up their room keys and were heading for the bank of elevators when Desmond announced,

'Just going to dump my suitcase and tidy up. I'll meet you at the bar in ten minutes.' Geordie's heart sank. He desperately wanted a quiet evening. Room service, a few phone calls and a mindless movie were what he had in mind. But no, his boss had other ideas, even though it was past eight and they'd travelled 2000 miles since lunchtime.

'OK, see you in 10 minutes.' Geordie exited on the 16th floor. He fumbled with his electronic keycard and entered a pleasant, if soulless room. He dumped his bags on the bed and quickly stripped to scrub off the day's grime in the shower. He changed into khaki slacks, a casual shirt, light jacket and loafers then headed to the elevators.

Desmond was well into his first Cutty Sark by the time Geordie reached the bar. The older man was away from home and raring to go. 'Ah, there you are. What do you want to drink?'

'I'll take a Bud Lite please.' He'd learned to pace himself on business trips. Desmond grimaced disapprovingly as Geordie ordered it from the waitress.

'Right,' Desmond started, 'we have various choices this evening.' Geordie hoped that one of those selections might be a "quiet night in", but suspected he'd be offered no such choice.

'First, we could go to the Top of The Mark and sip one of their famous Martinis while admiring a fabulous view of the Bay Area after dark.'

'I could live with that.'

'Or we could go to Chinatown and sample some oriental cuisine at the Nanking restaurant.'

'Sounds all right to me.'

'Or we could find a club and watch some ladies taking their clothes off.' Desmond raised a quizzical eyebrow, as if to say "I dare you".

Geordie remained poker-faced.

'Damned with faint praise, eh?' Desmond laughed.

'Or we could go to the Waterfront and listen to late-night blues at Pier 47.'

As the fatigued Geordie was weighing the options to appease his boss yet somehow contrive to be in bed by midnight, Desmond smacked the glass table conclusively.

'Right, here's what we'll do.' he announced, 'We'll do everything! We'll start at the Top of the Mark at the Mark Hopkins, followed by a meal at the Nanking. Then on the way to Pier 47 to listen to some blues, we'll pop into a couple of clubs and watch a few ladies removing their clothes. What do you think?'

Geordie assented unconvincingly, 'Sounds good to me.'

'Excellent.' Desmond signed the bar tab and they sauntered out to the Embarcadero taxi rank. Twenty minutes later they were settled in low window seats on the top floor of the Mark Hopkins Hotel, each sipping one of the bar's celebrated lemon Martinis. A luscious lady in a sequined green dress crooned Latin love songs, accompanied by a jazz pianist.

'Well, what do you think, Geordie?'

'It's a wonderful place. How do you know San Francisco so well?'

'When I was a recently-qualified young man I did stints at all our

international offices. San Francisco was one of them.'
Geordie was beginning to be comfortable with the ambience
when Desmond drained his Martini in a rush. 'Drink up. We have
places to go and people to see.' He settled the tab, they descended to
street level and hopped into a taxi.
'House of Nanking. 919 Kearny.'
The restaurant was crowded that night. They had to wait 20
minutes before being placed at a small table, cheek by jowl with
diners on either side. As Geordie studied the menu, Desmond
pronounced authoritatively, 'Everything's *good* at the House of
Nanking but the Won Ton soup is *famous.*'
Geordie was about to respond when a voice from the adjacent
table boomed, 'Desmond Thomson, my man! What on earth brings
you to this place?'
Geordie and Desmond were startled. They looked up to behold a
distinguished gentleman sitting at a table in the company of five other
well-dressed diners. Desmond looked blank.
'Peabody. Thatcher Q Peabody.'
'THATCH! What on earth are *you* doing here? It must be 30
years.'
'34 to be exact. I haven't seen you since just after we left
Corpus.' Thatcher Q Peabody had been a Rhodes Scholar at the same
Oxford college as Desmond. 'Not sure I'd have recognized you in
the street but I'd know that gravely voice until my dying day.'
Geordie was content to take a back seat at this jolly reunion of
old university pals; he enjoyed listening to their reminiscences and
got on with supping his famous Won Ton soup.
'One thing I've wondered about all these years.' Thatcher asked,
'What happened to your wine cellar?'
'Wine cellar? Good Lord, you've got a good memory.'
'Only for eccentric, creative and unusual people.'
Desmond turned to include Geordie in the conversation. 'When
I was 20 years old and about half way through my time at Oxford, I
inherited £2000 from my dear aunt. £2000 may not sound very much

today, but back then it enabled me to buy and run an Austin Healey and lay down a wine cellar. The car cost £750, if I remember correctly. I then called a vintner friend in the City off Leadenhall Market. I told him I had £1000 to invest and asked to him put down a selection of cases of wine and port, ready for consumption in 3 to 5 years. Back then you could buy a very reasonable Château wine or vintage port for 2 guineas a bottle, or £24 a case. He bought me 40 cases—30 cases of wine and 10 of port—and stored them in his cellars on my behalf.'

'Pretty impressive.' Geordie said, agog.

'Wait till you hear what he did next.' Thatcher egged on his old friend.

'Well, after 3 years a third of the wines were ready to drink. That was 10 cases, or 120 bottles of mature claret. I like drinking as much as the next man but reckoned I would only get through 60 bottles of claret in a normal year's drinking. The port could wait but I instructed my vintner friend to sell the 5 extra cases of mature wine. We made a good profit, which he then invested in 15 cases of the current year's vintage, ready for drinking in another 3 to 5 years' time.'

'And so it rolled on.' Thatcher said.

'Over the next ten years he built me a wonderful collection of wines. When I married we moved the wines from the cellarers to our own house. With his help I've never had to buy a bottle of decent wine since my Oxford days.'

'That's stupendous.' Geordie marvelled, 'Do you still play the game?'

'Not as ardently as I used to. We have several thousand bottles at various stages of maturity in our cellar. I'm drinking less than I used to, so when cases come to maturity I don't necessarily reinvest when I sell them.'

'Desmond is reaping the benefit of a classic long-term investment strategy. A few bucks on the table as a young man and he's never had to purchase a bottle of wine since.' Thatcher Q Peabody boasted to his admiring companions.

They finished their meal, swapped cards, swore eternal love and left the House of Nanking for the stews of San Francisco.

Geordie and Desmond proceeded to patronize not one, not two, but three strip joints. In each case they waited for the current act to wind down to see who was coming on next. In each case the second act was seedier, more tattooed and more silicon-enhanced than the first.

'Enough to put you off sex for life.' Desmond harrumphed. Geordie was not stimulated enough to take notice; he was dreaming of setting up his own wine cellar. Well past midnight they exited the third strip joint. They agreed to skip the blues bar and cabbed back to the Embarcadero.

Geordie drifted asleep to the idea of a portfolio of first-rate wines, some of which he would sell and some of which he would drink. He dreamed of the dinner parties he would host in the distant future. He looked forward to relating one day how he had emulated the great Desmond Thomson, built up a cellar and enjoyed a lifetime of fine drinking, essentially gratis.

When Geordie returned to London he tracked down the sales manager of a well-known wine merchant. His name was Ben Cormie; he was a lively character and very receptive to acting as Geordie's agent in this project.

'Here's what I'll do. Whenever I make a purchase of interesting wines for a big client, I will add on a couple of cases for you. That way you can ride along at wholesale prices. I'll store them with our cellarers, for which there will be a small annual charge. Then you can take them out when you're ready.'

'How will I keep tabs on this process?'

'I'll notify you whenever I buy something for you and you'll get a quarterly report from our accounts department. They'll list all the wines I've bought for you and show the cash balance on your account, if any. I suggest that we start buying straight away, so I'll need a cheque on account as soon as you're ready to start.'

'Excellent.' Geordie sent Ben a cheque with instructions 'to purchase wines and port at your discretion, with a view for consumption in three to five years.'

Soon he began to receive notes from Ben Cormie. 'Picked up four fabulous cases of Vieux Télégraphe today.', 'What about 2 cases of Léoville Barton?', 'A steal on three cases of Cockburns 1975 vintage port at the wine auction in South Ken.', 'Here's an amazing opportunity—not what you instructed, but I bought four bottles of 1756—yes, that's 1756—Verdalho at a clear-out sale of a Scottish castle yesterday. They're yours if you want them, but pricey.'

At this last suggestion Geordie baulked and concluded that he was on an investment mission to build a tradable wine cellar, not a stamp collection of rare wines. He would pass on this opportunity.

Big mistake: years later, a Shanghai investor purchased one of the bottles for $100,000 at auction. In the meantime, Ben Cormie couldn't resist the opportunity; he invited Geordie to his office the next time he was in London. On his desk sat an ancient green hand-blown glass squat bottle, its neck sealed tightly with wax. The label was still discernible after 250 years of a Scottish castle's damp and dust, and one could make out the flourish of a quill pen: Verdalho 1756. Ben cracked the wax through to the cork, which was surprisingly intact—it needed a modern corkscrew to pull it out. He poured a shot-glass of the viscous amber fluid.

'Be my guest.' He kindly offered Geordie the glass first.

Geordie lifted the glass gingerly and sniffed the bouquet, 'Smells promising.' He sipped the fluid. 'Absolutely amazing. It's sweet and you can still taste the grape. Here, you try it.' He handed the glass back to Ben.

'Sensational.' Ben savoured the ancient liquid. 'Do you realize,' his eyes drifted out to the leafy Georgian square beyond his office. 'This was in the bottle before General Wolfe beat the French in Québec, before Napoleon was born, before Nelson and Wellington, Queen Victoria and Charles Darwin. While all those wars raged in the 18th, 19th and 20th centuries, this unassuming bottle sat quietly on a shelf in an Argyll castle cellar waiting to be dusted off and tasted by thee and me in the 21st.'

Geordie was not offered a second glass; Ben would get industry-wide brownie points for sharing this bottle with other, more prestigious customers.

Six years into the project Ben had already sold most of the wines he'd bought initially for Geordie. Helped by the fact that Geordie was still based overseas and had not sampled any bottles on the way, the collection had expanded to 160 cases of top quality Bordeaux and Côtes du Rhône of varying maturities and 20 cases of vintage port.

Geordie duly returned to Scotland and ordered delivery. The liveried van—"By Appointment to HRH..."—made its way up the drive to Balnadarg to great anticipation. The men were instructed to put each case in a pre-ordained spot in the cellar, according to its date of optimal drinkability.

The van disappeared back down the drive on its all-night journey to London. Before the excitement had died down, Geordie descended to the cellar with a chisel and claw hammer. He selected a case at random, prised open the lid and beheld his booty. Each bottle was wrapped neatly in soft paper, on which was printed Châteauneuf-du-Pape Domaine du Vieux Télégraphe H. Brunier et Fils Propriètaires –Récoltants. He removed the paper and cradled the bottle like a puppy. Premier Prix au Concours de Dégustation....le 24 Avril 1982.

'A prizewinner...it doesn't get much better than this.' he exulted to himself.

He returned above deck brandishing the bottle to Josie. He nicked off the lead cap and extracted the cork in one accomplished manoeuvre. 'We may as well enjoy the fruits of all this accumulation of wines, don't you think? We'll let it get to room temperature and have it with our meal tonight.'

'This is delicious.' Josie sampled her glass.

'Light tannin, still quite young with a hint of herbs and soft fruit.' Geordie pronounced, as he lifted his glass to the candle-light.

'Just like you—quite young with a hint of herbs and soft fruit.' Josie laughed; she really had a way of keeping Geordie's hat size to scale. So they bantered happily through two courses and finished the bottle.

The aura began as they were clearing up after dinner. It was that familiar, dreaded blindness and incoherence that heralded Geordie's perennial nightmare: migraine. His well-practised routine was to swallow a blue pill and go to bed. But it wasn't sensible to take naratriptan hydrochoride after four glasses of red wine. The next two days were an orgy of vomiting, numbness and a skull-shattering headache.

'It can't have been the wine.' Geordie assured Josie a few days later. 'It was just a delayed reaction to that trip I did last week. Jetlag and business stress and all that stuff give me migraines.'

'Don't be so sure.' she replied. 'Red wine's a well-known trigger for migraine, along with caffeine and chocolate.'

'Maybe, but we'll give it another shot in the next few days.'

By way of experiment he purchased a bottle of cheap, light Argentinian red plonk at the local supermarket and they drank it over dinner one evening. It was refreshing and there was no ill-effect.

'See, it's not the red wine.'

A month later they had friends to dinner and Geordie opened three bottles of Château Grand Puy Lacoste 1978 . It was superb with the venison they served. As the tail lights of the guests' cars flickered down the drive, Geordie felt the familiar ominous numbness in his arm.

'Oh oh.'

Every bottle of exclusive château wine they sampled in the subsequent months had the same effect. Geordie was devastated. He couldn't bear to call his friend Ben and risk the ridicule of the wine world by selling his carefully-nurtured collection. He decided to hold on and pass the lot over to his son for his 18th birthday.

Seven years later Geordie threw the cellar key at William.

'Go for it, mate. Everything down there is for you.'

William made his way into the dank cellar and shouted up the staircase,

'Dad? I can't see anything in particular.'

'The wine, William. All the cases of booze are for you.'

'Wow, Dad, that's a lifetime's drinking.'

'Yup: over to you, mate. It should see you through university at any rate.'

That evening William opened a bottle of 1981 Château Cissac. After leaving it to acclimatize to room temperature he poured a glass. 'Yuck, Dad, it's corked.' He opened three other random bottles. All corked. Geordie had left the wine too long and it had gone off.

Embarrassed by the dubious gift he'd given his son, Geordie said defensively, 'Well at least you have the 20 cases of vintage port. Port never goes off.'

The following night William opened a bottle of 1975 Cockburn's Port.

'Thanks Dad, this is delicious.' After two glasses William became incoherent. 'I don't feel well... I can't see properly...my arms are numb.' The boy spent the next 48 hours retching and sweating and experiencing the joys of his first migraine.

'So the wines are corked and the port gives the boy migraines.' Josie could always be relied upon to summarize a situation succinctly.

'I'm beginning to understand that there must be a story behind those bottles of 1756 Verdalho they found in that castle in Argyll a few years ago.' Geordie replied glumly.

A few weeks later Geordie dropped into a nursing home outside Edinburgh to visit his old friend and mentor, Desmond Thomson. He was a frail old fellow, and had lost much of his intellectual capacity, but was still surprisingly on the ball on many subjects. As Geordie stood up to leave, the old man clasped his hand.

'One thing I've wondered about all these years.' He asked, 'Whatever happened to your wine cellar?'

Bowser's Last Stand

The doorbell rang. Geordie crossed the kitchen, tripped over a pile of boots, flung open the door and was confronted by the unexpected figure of Tam. Tam's vintage John Deere gurgled on the gravel, as patient as a plough horse munching oats in the crisp air. The tractor was hitched to an 8000 gallon cylindrical tank, its riveted plates bolted to the chassis of a Second World War vintage British army truck.

'Good Lord, is it that time again?'

'Aye Sir, every two years. The last Tuesday of February.'

'Well, you'd better come in for a cup of coffee then. I'm not quite ready.' Geordie led Tam into the kitchen. 'Have you met my wife, Josie?' She was gathering her papers off the table as they entered.

'Aye, we met the last time.' Tam stated with irrefutable accuracy. He reached to shake Josie's hand.

'Of course I've met Tam,' Josie looked piteously at her husband, 'At least a dozen times, I'd say.' She rolled her eyes, turning to the visitor. 'Afraid I can't stay and chat, I'm late for a meeting. Be sure you're tidier this time, Tam. I don't want to see any tracks on the grass, and keep out of the flowerbeds, all right?' Josie departed from the room briskly.

'No tracks on the grass this time,' Tam repeated sheepishly. He winced at Josie's understatement as he recalled the incident. Last time he was here the coupling on his tractor sheared and his fully - loaded bowser had rolled downhill, crossed the lawn, smashed through a line of cold frames and come to rest in the walled garden, sans wall.

Geordie flicked the switch on the kettle, unhooked a mug, extracted a teaspoon from a drawer and placed the coffee jar firmly on the counter beside the sugar bowl.

'Don't worry about it, Tam. That was two years ago. Here, help yourself. Milk's in the fridge, biscuits in the tin. I'll be back down in

five minutes.' He left Tam in the kitchen, cornered by two black Labradors wagging expectantly on hearing the magic word, "biscuit".

Tam stood by the window sipping his coffee. He wore clean blue dungarees, well-polished old brown brogues, a cotton check shirt and a woollen tie. His thick grey hair was cut in the style fashionable among ratings in the Royal Navy 40 years earlier. The sides of his head were trimmed to a martial stubble, the top swept back and flattened to a shine with hair oil. As a young man he was drilled to turn out sharply. Like many tradesmen of his generation who'd been through National Service he took particular pride in his appearance. He winced at the young workmen these days with electronic gadgetry stuck to their ears and anal cleavages on full display whenever they bent over.

Geordie reappeared in the kitchen wearing his flat cap, coat and boots.

'Sorry to keep you waiting Tam. How have you been since you were last here two years ago?'

'Always busy. I tried to retire but there's just so much to do. My son took over the contract business and he needs me to help out four or five days a week.'

'Yes- I remember now. You were about to retire when you came over last time. You were going to travel around the country in your caravan for a few months.'

'Aye-that never happened.' Tam shrugged with a tinge of regret. 'But maybe if my son could find some decent drivers then I'd go on my caravan trip.'

'Well, it's always a treat to see you back here on the job.' Geordie patted the older man's shoulder in a filial way. He didn't see any reason to say anything further of the incident that Josie had alluded to. It was an honest accident caused by metal fatigue, not carelessness, a long time ago. 'Ready to roll?'

'Aye. We'll start at the usual place.'

Geordie shut the house door behind them. Their breath condensed in the frosty air as soon as they walked outside. Tam heaved himself into the tractor cabin and Geordie clambered after him, wedging into the tight space just behind the driver's seat. Tam rammed the machine into gear, diesel fumes belched skywards and the ungainly procession lumbered along the drive to the first junction. They turned right towards a line of farm dwellings.

The first cottage was a Victorian gate lodge, its fading burgundy face-boards carved delicately with four-leaved clovers. They were peeled and rotten in places, but the overall effect was pleasantly quaint. In summer the old sandstone building nestled in the clasp of climbing roses, wisteria and honeysuckle. Geordie's tenant was a retired university lecturer in French; she lived alone with her Siamese cat. Regular with the rent, she kept the garden tidy and always had something cheerful to say.

Tam backed the tractor skilfully down a narrow path behind the building, positioning the bowser a few feet short of a manhole cover overgrown with weeds. They jumped out. Tam grabbed a claw hammer from the tool box under the tractor seat, levered up the manhole cover and flipped it heavily onto the grass. A crust of bacteriological goop lay on the surface of the septic tank.

Geordie peered in. 'Looks rather like the crumble on an apple pie'.

'Aye, looks healthy enough.' Tam concurred as he donned thick rubber gloves and linked together two lengths of heavy duty PVC suction pipe. He secured one end to the intake valve on the pump attached to the bowser and pushed the other into the depths of the septic morass. He returned to the tractor and engaged a lever. The John Deere roared to life, the power take-off driveshaft picked up to full speed and the pump was activated. A demonic sucking sound emanated from the sludge as two years of accumulated sewage transferred from the septic tank into the unspeakable guts of Tam's bowser.

'Aye, so it's been a busy year or two. I had trouble with the Department getting my pension sorted.' Tam leaned against the rounded side of the bowser. 'They told me one thing and they did another. They said I hadn't made enough insurance payments.'

'I'd have thought they had plenty of time to warn you about that over the years.'

'Aye, plenty of time. If you include my time in the Navy I've worked 52 years.'

The loose end of the pipe began to flip around the slimy bottom of the empty tank, greedily seeking more sewage to devour. Geordie fancied for a moment that he saw the rivets of the bowser strain as great volumes of air were forced into it under pressure. Tam hastened back to the tractor controls and turned off the driveshaft. The pump shuddered to a halt and the sucking stopped. Tam pulled the pipe from the tank, disconnected the sections and replaced them in the cradle on the side of his trailer. He rolled the steel cover back into position over the manhole, removed his gloves and climbed back into the tractor cabin. 'That's 600 gallons. Now to the Lodge at the West Gate.'

So they rumbled around the landscape from cottage to cottage, emptying each septic tank as mandated under the landlord's leases. Seven tanks were de-sludged, amounting to nearly 5,000 gallons of foul water.

One tank remained to be emptied — the monster stone-lined cesspool back at the big house, embedded 20 feet into the earth and containing the better part of 2000 gallons of sewage.

While they'd been driving about the estate, Geordie admired the solid efficiency with which Tam executed his task. He knew where the septic tanks were, backed up to them, flipped off their lids, pulled on his gloves, coupled the pipes, sucked out the contents, replaced the lids, decoupled the pipes, removed his gloves, hopped into the tractor and drove purposefully to the next tank.

Geordie respected Tam because he liked to deal immediately with problems cropping up in any of his tenants' sewage systems, but also because he simply liked being with a man who enjoyed his work.

Tam was equally pleased to have a companion to chatter with, because like many solitary folks he would talk incessantly whenever he got the chance. Although he claimed to be concerned about his pension, he admitted that he didn't really want to retire. 'I enjoy the banter with the lads. Some days I feel a wee bit creaky but by lunchtime I'm fine.' He complained about politicians of every stripe, loathed local councillors and, 'as for global warming, whatever that is ...'

Geordie interjected here and there but was content to let Tam's wind blow itself out.

As the tractor hauled its burgeoning cargo around the farm's rutted tracks, Geordie noticed, while staring idly behind the cab at the scenery, that brown effluent was leaking from rivet holes and flowing down the curved sides of the bowser. The tidal slosh of liquid inside was clearly audible above the growl of the tractor's engine.

'Don't you think, Tam, that the bowser is pretty full now? Would it not be best to empty it at the sewage plant and come back later to de-sludge the big house?'

'No, it's fine, we're well within capacity." Tam replied confidently. "It's got 3000 gallons of space yet, and your cesspool is only 2000, maximum. There's plenty of room in there.'

'I'm just a little concerned because the rivets are weeping down the outside of the bowser.'

'The rivets have wept since the day the bowser was made.' Tam replied knowingly.

'And when was that?'

'1946'.

'Fair enough,' Geordie's sceptical look wasn't observed by Tam. 'I'll defer to the experience and seniority of my companion.'

Tam turned the John Deere off the rutted track back onto the smooth tarmac of the main drive. The cumbersome trailer followed, accompanied by violent sloshing and sewage streaming from its rivets. For a moment, Geordie thought the whole caboodle would tip over.

'See, no problem at all,' Tam shifted up two gears and in a defiant cloud of tractor exhaust the noisome cavalcade chugged up the drive towards the Big House.

Their destination was a rambling country pile that had evolved through the centuries from vaulted medieval cellars to electronic sound systems, with traces of every period in between. The building today was unquestionably large but quite compact compared to a century earlier. Over the 20th century it was pruned on many occasions to make it more compatible with contemporary life styles and the cost of overheads. It sported double-glazed windows, a tight roof and new cast iron rainwater pipes to placate the heritage wallahs. Josie had supervised its decoration, inside and out. She had researched the Georgian materials and colours meticulously while trying to restore many features to their former glory.

The cesspool was located in a grassy dip about 30 yards off to the east of the house. Tam backed the bowser as closely as he could, stopping on the drive just opposite the drawing room, being particularly careful to stay on the gravel and avoid rolling a tyre over the lawn. He pulled five lengths of PVC pipe off the cradle, linked them together, connected one end to the pump intake and walked with the pipe across to the cesspool.

'I suppose I should know the answer to this,' ventured Geordie, 'but why is this one called a cesspool and all the others called septic tanks?'

'In the old days,' Tam explained, 'cesspools were used for sewage disposal but they hadn't yet understood how bacteria existed to break down the sewage. Foul water flowed into the cesspool, where it evaporated or soaked away as it overflowed. Or sometimes the raw sewage just flowed from the cesspool into the sea or a river. They were horribly messy places. Then some old English vicar observed that if you let the sewage sit in the tank for a while, bacteria will break down the sewage. If you provide a soak away channel from an overflow pipe, by the time the waste has been digested by the bacteria in the tank and soaked into the ground the water cleans itself."

'I see,' Geordie replied, impressed by Tam's grasp of the subject.

'Actually, your cesspool was modified into a septic tank 40 years ago. They just never got round to changing its name'.

Tam pushed the mouth of the pipe through the crust into the depths of the cesspool. Geordie felt curiously vulnerable, embarrassed even, for allowing a stranger to penetrate the contents of his family sewage tank. A horribly revealing object might float up in the bacterial soup, something shockingly foul that shone an unimaginable light on his character. What, he couldn't imagine; his conscience was clear of course, but an indefinable anxiety niggled at him.

As Tam strode back to the tractor, Geordie peered nonchalantly into the cesspool. It had the same crust as all the other septic tanks — nothing special here. He wondered about all the foul stuff underneath the crust, invisible to the casual eye. He then reasoned that whatever might lurk in there, it would shortly be blended indistinguishably with everyone else's septic proceeds in the safety of Tam's bowser. This made him feel better.

The familiar oily diesel exhaust cloud shot into the air, fleetingly obscuring the windows at the side of the house. The tractor engine revved loudly as Tam activated the driveshaft and started the pump. It began sucking and he strolled back to the cesspool to join Geordie. Tam was already talking as he approached.

'I heard a radio programme on my way here this morning. They were talking about politicians' ages. You know, some are even young enough to be my grandchildren. What could they possibly know?'

'You shouldn't let it bother you,' Geordie replied off-handedly. He was more fascinated by the vortex of sewage spinning sluggishly in the tank at his feet. It recalled a chocolate-making machine he'd seen once in New York.

'But it *does* bother me, because it's too late for me to do anything or make a difference to the country.'

'Tam, that's ridiculous. Look at everything you've done in the community during your working life over the past 52 years. Besides, you were in the Royal Navy, serving your country, which is more than most people can say these days. Think of all the help you've given, all the laughs you've had with your friends. You led your champion Galloway bulls into the ring at least ten times.' Tam's prize bulls had been a regular part of local agricultural shows for years. 'You're involved in umpteen church committees, you even dug graves for nothing during the strikes in the 1970's, you took poor kids on expeditions into the mountains ...'

'I might have won the prize for breeding the best bull in the show, but nobody ever asked my opinion about what really matters. Everything is such a mess now, I should have paid more attention and got more involved. I'm sure the world would think I'm too old now, but I could give so much advice on so many things'.

Geordie put his arm around Tam's shoulder for the second time that day. 'First and foremost, Tam, you are not too old. It's never too late to get involved. There are lots of examples of brilliant older politicians all over the world. Look at Mandela, Mao, Castro, Mitterand, Churchill. If you feel you must get involved you should do so. I'll support you, Tam.'

Tam smiled, 'That's a fine thing to say.'

'On the other hand, you are more valuable and have accomplished more than any politician, Tam. I'm not sure you want to compare yourself to politicians. Most of them end up as broken men, despised and ridic....."

Geordie's rhetorical flourish was interrupted as he spotted the PVC pipe at the bottom of the cesspool flailing around for lack of sewage to suck from the empty tank. Their attention had wandered from the task at hand.

'Tam, I think you should go back to the tractor and turn off the pump.'

'But that's the point,' Tam completely disregarded Geordie's suggestion. 'So many politicians are despised. I could bring experience and common sense to the country. I'd speak for farmers, and the armed forces too. I'm sure I could make a difference.'

'Tam, I'm sure you could.' Geordie replied nervously as the bowser began to judder visibly from the intake of forced air. 'But I really think you should go and turn off the pump. We can discuss your political future afterwards.'

The pipe flip-flopped around the bottom of the tank like a floundering catfish, gasping for traction and sucking air along its 30 yard length back to the bowser. The high speed rotating driveshaft whined, the pump coughed and screamed, forcing ever more air into the tank already brimming with sewage.

'It's always been a matter of pride that we do things right in our family.' Tam persisted. 'After the Royal Navy, my brothers became craftsmen, my mother was a nurse and my sisters were teachers. We all did our time as apprentices and learned to do things properly. How many people in our government are qualified to do anything useful?'

'You should be proud of yourself, Tam,' Geordie wasn't sure what had triggered Tam's sudden inspiration for a late-life career change, but he perceived a more immediate problem. 'If you don't mind, I'm going back to the tractor right now to turn off that pump. There's going to be an accident'.

He left Tam contemplating the hole and headed back towards the bowser. As has often been observed at the scene of disasters, Geordie would later recall that everything began to unfold in slow motion. He was about half way across the lawn when Josie emerged from the house, waving her arms, running towards him and shouting something indistinguishable across the metallic clanking of the overheating pump. He guessed the drift of what she was trying to convey.

He accelerated to a sprint towards the tractor. A hard object whizzed like a bee past his head and whacked into a tree behind him. He could clearly see the galvanized steel plates of the bowser respiring in and out like the flanks of an asthmatic rhinoceros. Rivets popped out with a ping! and flew in random directions. Glass shattered as they cracked through window panes in the house like shrapnel. Fragments of metal hit the pristine masonry on the walls with a sharp smack and a puff of dust. The glass lamp above a side door took a direct hit and exploded into fragments. Sewage began to spurt from the rivet-holes as the entire bowser juddered on its chassis.

The joints in the steel plates cracked simultaneously. There was a momentary implosion, followed by a massive explosion. The bowser disintegrated, sending ruptured steel plates spinning crazily into the air. One section crashed onto the roof of the house, where it hung off the gutter after scraping a furrow down at least twenty rows of slates. Oily smoke and a tongue of flame shot out of the back of the tractor. Geordie dived onto the lawn and braced himself for the white heat of a fireball. An instant later he was hit instead by a brown wall of sewage. While it had the happy effect of snuffing out the tractor's incipient explosion, Josie was knocked off her feet by it as she ran towards Geordie.

When the wave had passed the laird and his wife lay together on the lawn in a pool of foetid sludge enveloped in an indescribable, nauseating stench. Geordie pulled Josie unsteadily to her feet. She was covered by streaks of soggy toilet paper and sewage was matted into her hair. She stood motionless like a dripping scarecrow; her eyes wide open and sporting an other-worldly smile. Behind the couple lay the wreckage of the bowser and the smouldering tractor. A wide streak of sewage was plastered across the front of the freshly-painted house from roof to basement. Wet wads of toilet paper festooned the window sills, the gutters and shrubbery.

Tam stood in mute horror for a moment, surveyed the scene of utter ruination and came running towards the pair.

'Are you all right?' he shouted 'For heaven's sake, Mrs Kinloch, you shouldn't have come running this way. What a disaster!'

'Well Tam, there's your answer'. Geordie shouted back. 'You are definitely cut out to be a politician. First, you ask a stupid question, then you blame someone else, then you state the obvious.'

'There... are... two ways we can handle this,' Josie began slowly, flicking a wad of toilet paper off her arm. 'We can weep, or...' She began to chuckle, then fell on her hands and knees on the grass in a fit of uncontrolled laughter.

The Kinwhirrie Cat

'I've brought you some daffodils.' Geordie raised the flowers for her to see and placed them on the sideboard by the bed. 'I picked ninety: one for each year you've been alive, and one for luck.'

The Filipino nurse scooped them from him, arranged them in a vase and positioned it on the sideboard. She then left the room, closing the door gently behind her.

'Bless you,' his mother smiled weakly. 'Are they from Balnadarg?'

Geordie pulled a wicker chair up to the bed and kissed her cheek. It hurt him to see the severe bruising on the back of her hand caused by intravenous needles.

'Yes, they were growing in the woods a mere twenty minutes ago.' He plucked a stem out of the vase for her to see sticky slime oozing from the cut. 'As fresh as they can be.'

'How is the family? '

'Everyone as busy as ever. How about you? How are you feeling?'

'Oh, I can't remember much from one day to the next, but they're very nice here. I had a good lunch today.'

Geordie had moved his mother to this small rural hospice with an unspoken dread, still hoping that she might recover sufficiently to return to Balnadarg. At least the hospice sat in familiar countryside; the window in her room looked across a wooded glen filled with daffodils and a dreamy view of the distant hills beyond. She was well cared-for and warm.

'Yes? What did they give you?'

'I can't remember, but I do know it was good,' she said appreciatively, 'And there was lots of it.'

'Excellent.'

They sat silently for a few minutes as Geordie racked his head for something interesting to say. He adored his mother but hated the strained banter to which their relationship lately seemed to have degenerated. There was a reason for this, of course. His maddening sense of decorum forbade him from even remotely discussing why his mother now lay in a hospice.

There was a click and the door to the room opened noiselessly. An untidy black fluffy cat appeared. Tufts of moss and wood shavings clung to her underside. She glided directly across to Geordie, wound herself around his legs, gave a muted 'miaow' and jumped onto his mother's bed. She padded around the blankets before settling comfortably at the foot of the bed, for all the world as if she had slept there all her life.

'You never told me about your friend.'

'I've never seen this cat in my life before.' his mother replied.

'I find that hard to believe,' Geordie smiled. 'She's completely at home curled up at the end of your bed.' He stretched across to scratch the cat's ears and was rewarded with a contented purr. 'Pretty scruffy, though. She looks as if she lives in a barn. She could do with a good wash.'

'You're not supposed to wash cats. They wash themselves.' On cue, the cat stretched out her right foreleg and began licking her paw with a long rasping motion of her tongue.

Their conversation drifted towards family and what Geordie's teenagers planned to do the following summer: Croatia. They talked about the upcoming election and the issues that were at stake in "the most critical election of the century", according to party propaganda he'd seen lying around. His mother had not lost the power of observation.

'When I was a girl, poor children had rickets from malnutrition. Now they have diabetes from over-eating.'

'Yes, there's a whole new list of problems these days compared to the old days.' Geordie ventured. Despite the promising start she would not be drawn into further polemics.

'I want to go home, Geordie.'

'You're here to get better. As soon as you recover your strength

you can come home.' He knew he was lying, but wished it were true.
'Why can't I come home and get better in my own room?'

'Because you've been very sick and the nurses here are trained
to take care of you. We don't have the facilities at home if something
were to happen to you.'

'I still want to come home. I'll be all right there.' She squeezed
his hand faintly, conveying her pitiful frailty and vulnerability as
strongly as she could.

'As soon as you're strong enough, I'll come and pick you up and
we'll go home. I promise.'

'Soon, Geordie. Please.'

'When you're well enough, I promise.'

There was a bustle of activity in the hospice corridor as the trolley
rolled up and tea trays were prepared for the patients. The door swung
open and the Filipino nurse entered the room again with a broad grin.
'I bring you a cup of tea, Mr Kinloch.'

'That's very kind of you.'

She laid the tin tray on the sideboard beside the daffodils. It held
two milky cups of tea and four flat dry scones that resembled hockey
pucks. As she turned towards Geordie with a grin full of gold teeth
the nurse spotted the cat. The creature had licked her way
methodically around her limbs and was now washing her fourth—
and last—paw. It was a heart-warming domestic portrait: a son
visiting his elderly mother, a cat lying contentedly at her feet, and a
battered carriage clock ticking away the hours. It would be hard to
imagine a more ageless and comforting scene.

The scream that ensued was like a clip from Psycho. An
expression of fathomless terror overwhelmed the nurse as she raised
her hands to her face.

'*El Gato! El Gato! El Gato!*' she screamed.

'For heaven's sake it's only a cat. I can understand a mouse,
but...'

She didn't wait for more of Geordie's light-hearted facetiousness
and burst out of the door. She ran hysterically along the corridor as

if she were escaping a rabid vampire with a chainsaw, shouting *'El Gato! El Gato! El Gato!'*

Nurse Mackinnon came steaming up the corridor like a destroyer on full battle stations, heels clacking on the linoleum, thermometers rattling and starch crinkling. 'What ON EARTH is going on?' she barked accusingly at Geordie, as if he had made a pass at one of her nurses.

'Well, nothing that I can fathom.' he responded sheepishly. 'The nurse came in, left a tea tray, saw the cat and freaked out.' He nodded towards the bed.

Nurse Mackinnon whipped round and saw the black fluffy creature curled happily at his mother's feet. She calmed instantly and nodded knowingly, 'Ah, the Kinwhirrie Cat.'

His mother seemed amused by the commotion. She'd raised herself on her pillows and was waiting eagerly for the next round of this unexpected drama. Her eyes were brighter than Geordie had seen for a while.

'She hasn't been here at the hospice for a month or so,' Nurse Mackinnon spoke quietly. She turned to Geordie. 'Mr Kinloch, perhaps you would come outside for a moment?' She held the door handle and gestured for Geordie to go into the corridor. She closed the door behind them.

'It's quite strange, Mr Kinloch, and may seem odd in this modern day and age. I feel rather embarrassed to speak to you like this ...'

Geordie was agog. Far more than he'd bargained for on this outing to visit his mother. 'Yes..?' he was hanging on her every word.

'Yes. Whenever the Kinwhirrie Cat comes into the hospice and sits on someone's bed, they die within a few hours. We don't know how she gets into the building and nobody has ever seen her around the place. Except, of course, when someone is about to die.'

'I see.' Geordie said sombrely. 'So that means ...'

'I'm afraid so, if the past is any guide, Mr Kinloch. I'm so terribly sorry.'

He almost warmed to the old battle-axe. 'I see but... why the

Kinwhirrie cat?'

'The farm next door is called Kinwhirrie and we just assumed that she came from there. But a year ago after a spate of visits from the cat and ensuing deaths I went over to ask if they'd lost this rather endearing black fluffy cat. They had no knowledge of her. It's a bit puzzling. We do know that she's a very affectionate cat; she's certainly not feral and seems to comfort people a great deal. But nobody knows her outside the hospice and nobody knows how she gets in.'

'It all sounds a bit of a mystery.'

'Yes, it's not as if she's some sort of evil harbinger of unexpected death. Every person who has died after a visit from her has been calm and peaceful at the end ...and that includes quite a few difficult and troubled patients who have ended their lives in a peaceful way.'

'Were any of the deaths unexpected?'

'No, not really, not at all. The deaths have all been of very old or sick people whose time, quite simply, had come.'

Geordie snapped from the theoretical to this rather bizarre reality of the Kinwhirrie Cat.

'I should get back to my mother, if you don't mind. It appears that she doesn't have much time.'

'Yes of course Mr Kinloch. And again, I'm terribly sorry.'

Geordie returned to his mother's room. She was propped on the pillows as he'd left her. Her eyes were closed and there was a serene smile at the corners of her mouth. Her hands lay crossed on the sheet in front of her. Her skin was pale and waxy, almost luminescent. Beside her feet on the bed was a nest-like hollow, scraps of moss and a few wood shavings. The cat had gone.

A Rural Idyll

It amused Geordie when his metropolitan friends came to stay. At some point of their visit, usually after a good dinner on the second night, the conversation would drift wistfully, like a punt in the reeds, towards Geordie's good fortune for living in the seclusion of the Scottish countryside.

'You have no idea how lucky you are to be living such a peaceful existence at this stage of your life,' Ian Wingate began.

'Mmm.' Geordie smiled amiably, tapping the ash off his well-lit cigar into the glowing fireplace. 'Go on.'

'It must be wonderful to live in the middle of all this while you're still young enough to enjoy it. Do you have any idea how stressful City life is these days? I mean, I'm up at 6.30 every morning, in the office by 8.15. Work like a Trojan until noon, attend a business lunch, back at my desk at 2.30 and work until 6 most evenings. I generally don't get home until past 7.'

Home, for Ian Wingate, was a luxury penthouse in a fashionable block overlooking the Thames in Chelsea. Magnificent French windows opened onto a wide balcony with stunning river views. A broad parasol covered a teak table where, in fine weather, Ian and his family were served dinner by a Filipino couple, as often as not accompanied by several bottles of vintage Moët from the cooler.

'Then what?' Geordie asked.

'Oh, Laetitia runs the calendar. two or three nights a week we have engagements of one sort or another. Last week it was The Royal Ballet, a business dinner with a couple of Russians and their floozies. What else? Oh yes, a charity function at the V&A.' Ian recalled.

'That's quite a relentless agenda.' Geordie agreed, reminiscing wickedly that Ian Wingate's second wife had been called Titty by her intimates at university.

'You have *no* idea.'

Geordie made the right noises to encourage Ian to go on and

catalogue details of his hard-grinding London life. While appearing attentive and staring at the dancing flames in the fireplace, Geordie recollected some recent experiences in his idyllic rural life.

Scottish native red squirrels were under threat from verminous non-native grey squirrels, so the government was encouraging landowners to trap and eradicate the greys. As in every aspect of farming, the government had clear rules about how to undertake the extermination process.

Trapping a grey squirrel was the easy bit. Despatching it under the law was another matter. Geordie had no specific quarrel with these creatures. There was not a single animal, bird, reptile, insect or plant he hated enough to kill; even Japanese knotweed and bankers had a purpose under God, he felt sure.

The captured creature would be squirming in a hessian sack. Wearing thick gloves, Geordie would secure the squirrel by manoeuvring it into a corner of the sack. Then—this is exactly what was written in the instructions—locate the back of the head and, ensuring that it was against a hard surface, using a heavy fishing priest, deliver a rapid blow of sufficient force to fracture the skull.

'So while we're slogging our guts out at the bank,' Ian Wingate's monologue continued, 'you have complete freedom to do what you want each day: reading all those Russian and French novels, going for nice walks with the dogs in the fresh air…'

Geordie's 'Mmm' encouraged Ian to bang on heedlessly about this supposed Arcadian life.

Nine months earlier a tenant had complained of an overflowing septic tank. Geordie arranged for it to be pumped out, or de-sludged as was called in the trade. The invoice from the de-sludging contractor was accompanied by a hand-written note. It complained that the septic system had been overwhelmed by thick grease affecting the incoming pipe, the tank and the soak-away pipe. 'I've never seen such an abused tank in 20 years.'

The septic tank had been used without a break since it was built in the 1930's, serving generations of occupants. Diplomatically,

Geordie asked the tenant to be careful about what was put into the drain. Please, no animal fats, bio-detergents, cat litter, tampons or waste food. It was a reasonable request, he thought, but the tenant slammed the door, screaming that no landlord had the right to dictate his lifestyle.

A month later the tank was clogged again. Again Geordie paid £150 to have it de-sludged. Again the contractor complained that there had been severe mistreatment of the drainage system. Geordie knocked on the door, cap in hand, obsequiously offering His Supreme Tenantship a page that he'd downloaded from the internet: Dos and Don'ts of Septic Tanks. The tenant scrunched up the page and threw the ball into Geordie's face, threatening to take him to court for criminal harassment as he slammed the door again.

A month later the tank was seeping its noxious grey liquid again over the back yard of the cottage. Geordie refused to have it de-sludged this time, telling the tenant that he was no longer responsible for the consequences of such an egregious abuse of the system. The tenant turned white with rage, vowing to clear his name of Geordie's heinous accusations.

Two weeks later Geordie received a recorded delivery notice under the Fuck the Landlord (Scotland) Act in which he was ordered to appear before a tribunal to answer two allegations. First, that he had failed to provide his tenant with essential services up to the proper standard. Second, that he had engaged in criminal harassment of his tenant.

The tribunal consisted of a grey group of flint-faced paralegals, chaired by a woman. It was wondrous to behold how the case inexorably marched to its foregone conclusion. After a show trial worthy of Moscow in the 1930s, Geordie was given a month to install a new septic tank system. Despite working beautifully for 75 years the existing tank was deemed 2cms too short and 1.5cms too narrow under current building regulations. The tribunal threw out any suggestion of contributory negligence on the part of the tenant. The poor downtrodden man and his son smirked in the aisles: a signal victory for the wee folks against the breathtaking arrogance of their landlord. Justice was only partially served, however. Despite the tenant's damning allegations, the tribunal acquitted Geordie of the charge of criminal harassment. At least he didn't end up in the slammer.

'I love the box hedges that define the garden, and the way the honeysuckle grows through them,' Ian Wingate gushed.

'Yes, the fragrance is intoxicating, particularly on a warm summer evening'. Geordie's comment triggered further monologue. Ian was content to drone on with ever more observations of the country gentleman's lifestyle, oblivious of Geordie's aloofness from the conversation.

The previous week, Geordie had encountered a band of teenagers sauntering along the drive towards the house. Two boys were swinging sticks, decapitating wild flowers and whacking young trees; a trail of empty cans, fag ends and litter marked their progress. The kids looked increasingly shifty as Geordie approached them with Virgil, his black Labrador, pottering harmlessly beside him.

When finally they met, Geordie told them they were most welcome to walk here, but please would they respect the wild flowers and kindly not drop litter. The teenagers did not stand back, but crowded close to Geordie, led by one of the boys with a stick. He was reminded of a scene on the veldt where he'd once watched a buffalo surrounded by hyenas. They nipped, bared their fangs, testing the buffalo relentlessly for weakness in its defences. The boy hissed,

'There's nae sich thing as private any more.'

'Not quite, my friend.' A growl from Virgil; Geordie wheeled round. The second boy's arm was raised to hit him from behind with his stick. Geordie sidestepped; Virgil barked. Hackles rising, he jumped instinctively between Geordie and the boy. Snarling, Virgil crouched to the ground like a panther. The boy dropped his stick and put up his hands in appeasement.

'Whoa, keep yer hair on, pal.'

'I suggest you all go home.' Geordie stood up to the teenage wolf pack as Virgil edged towards them, snarling. The kids broke and ran. Geordie remained standing on the drive, two sticks and four empty soda cans on the grass verge beside him. With a final woof! Virgil lost interest in hostilities and went back to snuffling through the hedgerows for rabbits.

'And the locals are so nice.' Ian re-emerged into Geordie's reverie. 'They're so genuine. Everybody knows everyone in the community. People all say good morning when you pass them in the village. You should compare that to London or New York, where the only people who pay attention to you on the street are beggars if you're lucky, muggers if you're not.'

'Yes, the locals are delightful. There's something reassuring when you have that sense of community.' Geordie agreed.

'It must be so wonderful in the spring when the lambs are born, nibbling on the fresh grass. You can wander over to the field and lean on the gate watching the pure joy of new lives …'

Geordie recalled the heartbreak of finding his favourite lamb, wee Bob, with his eyes pecked out by buzzards. He thought of Bob's mother, dear Vanessa, and the long nights from February to April when he and Josie had taken it in turns to stay up for the lambing.

'As for the house!' Ian Wingate drained his fourth glass of 1975 vintage port. 'A place like this would cost millions down south. You have no idea how lucky you are to live in a place like this.'

Eighteen months earlier, Geordie had found fragments of broken slate on the ground after an October storm. He called Jimmy the Roof. Two weeks later he turned up, an enormous chap about 6 foot 3 weighing 250 pounds. He squeezed through a skylight and popped onto the steeply-pitched roof with the grace of a champagne cork. With impressive alacrity for such a large man, he wandered fearlessly across the slippery surface. Here and there he selected a slate and snapped it like a wafer. He then reached into the underlying woodwork and came up with fistfuls of sawdust. He tested every part of the roof this way, then sat on the roof ridge to write in his notebook.

Geordie had been watching Jimmy's survey from the garden far below. He waited until he could contain his curiosity no longer, shouting,

'Well?'

'Well, Mr Kinloch, I don't know quite how to put this.'

'Try.'

'Very well, sir. Yer rufe's fucked.'

Eleven months and several hundred thousand pounds later, Balnadarg's roof was good for another hundred years with new cast-iron guttering, 76 tons of Welsh slate, lead ridges and gulleys, oak beams, half an acre of new sarking and an array of highly-priced replacement roof windows.

The decanter, which had passed back and forth between the friends, was now empty. Geordie rose unsteadily and threw two large logs into the embers amidst a shower of sparks; he placed the steel-meshed guard before the fire. Ian Wingate slumbered peacefully in his chair, no doubt dreaming of the idyllic rural life. It was nearly 2 o'clock.

'Good night old chap. I have to go to bed or I'll never be up on time for the Organic Audit Officer at 8 o'clock. Then I have to organize the removal of those 20 ancient trees that fell in last month's gales. See you in the morning.'

Ian Wingate slumbered on.

The Accidental Shepherd

'How can we possibly live on a farm and not raise sheep?' Josie asked.

'Fine, but who'll take care of them, pay the vet, mate them, lamb them, feed them?' Geordie responded irritably.

'I will, of course.'

'...Mend the fences, treat infections, move them around the fields, shear them, steer them through the sheep dip, then do all the paperwork for our friends in Brussels?'

'You've made your point. I've already told you, *I* will take care of the sheep.' Josie said emphatically, while managing to keep her voice at a reasonable pitch.

'All right, all right, can we please run through your business plan again?' Geordie was putting up his familiar smokescreen when he was dubious about a project.

'For the third time,' Josie raised her eyebrows in exasperation, but was careful to keep her voice down. 'there's a niche at the top of the market for high quality organic wool to make clothes and accessories for people who care about such things. If we developed a pedigree flock and treated the sheep incredibly well, this farm could become the benchmark for good husbandry. We would make a good living by selling top-quality wool for luxury production. We'd keep some wool for our own needs and sell the rest to Italians to make their ten thousand dollar suits.'

'That's a business *idea,* not a business *plan.*' he said, exasperated.

'Look, I love sheep as much as the next man, and I'll help when I can, but please don't expect to rely on me in this project. I'm simply too busy with other things.'

'Does that mean yes?'

'It means I won't get in your way. It's entirely your project.'

'Fantastic. I'm just going to call the agent and I'll be back in a moment.'

Josie returned to the room 15 minutes later. 'That's it. The agent is going to release the Bowmonts next Monday.'

'The Bowmonts?'

'Haven't you been reading your Ministry newsletters? Bowmonts were bred by a chap from the Macaulay Institute at Aberdeen University. He was trying to upgrade wool quality in Scotland, so produced this Merino/Shetland hybrid. His idea was to marry the Shetland's legendary hardiness with the Merino's legendary woolliness. It's a brilliant idea. Bowmonts are beautiful sheep. Here, look at this photo.'

Josie showed Geordie the photograph of a magnificent ram. The creature stood four-square on the grass, as primed as a prize fighter ready to despatch all comers.

'Look at that thick coat of wool, his amazing battering-ram head and his aristocratic posture.' she cooed.

'Fine, but how do you get the wool off the bugger?'

'We'll find out, won't we? I've just bought him and ten ewes.'

'Oh Lord.'

The following Monday a livestock transport truck edged slowly up the drive and backed into the small field behind the house. Geordie was struck by the spring in the driver's step as he activated the hydraulic ramp to release the sheep.

A dainty ewe nosed down the ramp. She was cautious at first, then gathered speed and leaped to the ground. She bucked and kicked when she reached the grass, reminiscent of Gene Kelly in a 1950's musical. Three more ewes followed, each demonstrating the same agility when leaping off the ramp. They counted ten ewes.

'Is that it?' inquired Geordie, who was witnessing the goings-on with amused detachment.

'Not quite.' the driver replied.

A heavy-footed thud came from inside. It was different from the metallic click-click, like the sound of high-heeled shoes, made by the ewes. This sound was more portentous, a sort of tectonic rumbling.

'Come on Herbie, git a move on.' The driver banged the side of the truck with the flat of his hand. The thudding gathered pace, then ceased. The beast appeared at the top of the ramp. He was even mightier than his photograph had suggested, with perfectly symmetrical curlicue horns; he was the very profile of a Spanish grandee wrapped in a cloud of wool. He stood framed at the exit like a cowboy crashing a bar after kicking in the door, then charged down the ramp into the field.

'What attitude.' Josie said admiringly. Geordie couldn't help agreeing.

'Sign here, please.' The laconic driver handed Josie a pink delivery slip. The hydraulic ramp folded back into the vehicle. She signed where instructed.

'Congratulations.' the driver tipped his cap as he clambered back into the cab. 'You now own the last flock of Bowmonts in the world.' He reflected for a moment, then added, 'Well, almost.'

'Oh.' was all Josie could say.

'And for very good reason.' He smirked, wound up his window and drove off.

'What did he mean by that?' she asked Geordie. She didn't think the driver had been the sort of chap who'd make a comment without a great deal of thought.

The sheep had found their way to the far end of the field and begun to graze. Josie and Geordie walked slowly towards them. The ewes were not troubled by the proximity of humans. The ram was leery, preferring to keep a good distance. They had thick coats, with the wool pulled well over their faces, showing only white noses and black eyes, as if they wore heavy balaclava hats. This was the Merino side of their breeding. Shetlands had more clearly-discernible faces, often black, with the wool bunching behind their ears but not beyond.

'Do we need to feed them?' Geordie asked.

'No, there's enough grazing in this field for another few months, then we'll need to top up with sheep feed.'

'So what do we need to do now?'

'Let nature take its course. The ewes come into season in October and Herbie will start to mate with them.' she said.

'Just like that?'

'Well, we'll have to monitor the process. We'll need to catch him in a few weeks and paint his chest and stomach with blue dye. When all the ewes have blue dye on their rear ends we'll know they've been mated and we can move them into a different field.'

'How d'you know all this stuff?'

'I read the instruction book. Also I've got quite friendly with the vet. She told me what to look for. Oh—and I've enrolled you into a lambing course next January.'

'I told you I didn't want to be involved in this project.'

'You're not involved. If you know how to do lambing, you could save lives if the vet's not around. It's like First Aid: everyone should know a bit of First Aid, particularly on a farm.'

Three weeks later Josie had borrowed an assortment of interlocking metal fences and created a pen with a wide entrance in a corner of the field. This was to be the centre of operations for the team, which had gathered early that morning for the job.

'The trick to catching the ram is to isolate him into this part of the field without him feeling cornered.' Josie advised Geordie and the handful of amused teenagers.

'Now, if the three of you take the dog and walk slowly in line between the ram and the flock, I'll walk up there with the others. We'll steer him gently towards the entrance of the pen. You've got to be slow and don't make any sudden movements.'

The first stage of the manoeuvre worked like a dream. The ram tracked steadily in front of the line, grazing warily as he went. He just liked to keep his distance from people. Josie closed in on him from the opposite direction and he made his way unwittingly through the entrance of the pen.

Whether it was a quick movement caused by the general rush to close the entrance, or the dog straying too close, it suddenly dawned on the fellow that he'd been nudged into a trap. In a flash he metamorphosed from unassuming woolly ruminant into a hundred kilograms of muscular fury. He charged, horns down, hit the metal fence with a fearsome clang and smashed through like a bullet through custard. Geordie's team scattered in undignified terror. The ram bolted to the far end of the field, turned to face them and snorted in defiance if anyone so much as stepped in his direction.

'So what's Plan B?' Geordie surveyed the chaos with an ill-disguised smirk.

'We need to call Jock.' Josie would not rise to her husband's implied told-you-so.

Jock was born in a Highland croft and had lived and breathed sheep all his life. He'd worked on sheep stations in Australia and advised Caribbean governments on sheep multiplication programmes. Somewhere along the line he had picked up a Legion d'Honneur. Like all true heroes he never talked about it.

Jock turned up at the field that afternoon. After a brief conversation with Josie, he released a Border collie from the back of his Land Rover. Responding to three whistles the dog singled out the ram and rounded it into the pen in less than two minutes. Jock closed the gate.

'Anything else, ma'am?'

'Well, since you're here...'

Jock flipped over the indignant beast with the ease of a pet guinea pig and daubed his belly with heavy blue dye.

'It's a crude but effective way of telling whether he's working the ewes—or anything else, for that matter. It's not uncommon to see every tup in the field buggered by a ram, all with blue erses, and none of the ewes being touched. Ye'd be surprised how many rams prefer the boys to the girls.'

'What do you do with those rams?' Geordie was curious.

'They go to the market. They're always good for rack of lamb and sheepskin slippers.'

Geordie was struck by the normality of life and death on the farm, but warmed to the lore of old Jock. There was more to sheep than he'd ever imagined. Herbie did his job and all the ewes duly became pregnant. The instruction book had advised removing the ram from the ewes at this stage, so they separated him into a neighbouring field. The ram hung around by the gate and never left the boundary fence; he wanted to be close to his ewes.

'He's pining away.' Geordie felt for the creature. 'What conceivable harm could he do to the ewes if they were all in the same field together?'

Nobody had an answer, so they released the lonely ram back into the field with the ewes. It was touching to witness the welcome he received. The ewes ran over to nuzzle him and they spent the days grazing together. Not for ewes the jealousies of the harem.

The first lamb was born unexpectedly on a bitter morning in early March. He lay steaming on the frosty grass beside his mother, who was licking and trying to nudge him to his feet to get his circulation going. Josie picked him up gingerly and carried him to a warm shed, with the ewe following. The lamb wobbled to his feet and after being helped to locate his mother's teats, began feeding, his tail flickering with delight.

By mid-March twelve new lambs had entered the world: eight singles and two sets of twins. While he had dutifully attended the lambing course, Geordie's midwifery skills had not been required. Bowmonts turned out to be easy mothers. He became involved in the daily feeding ritual, however, pouring feed into low troughs. He loved watching the sheep running to their positions along the line of troughs. The ram was a true gentleman, always holding back for his girls to eat first. Geordie put a separate pile of feed on the ground nearby, in case there was not enough for him after the ewes had eaten at the troughs.

Jock showed up from time to time to see how Josie, his protégée, was faring in the sheep world. Without saying anything it was clear that he thought the Kinloch establishment was more of a country retreat than a working farm.

Seeing the lambs in the warm shed cavorting in clean, dry straw, he advised: 'You can let these lambs into the field now. A wee bit of frost will harden them up.'

In response Geordie and Josie opened the door latch and shooed the lambs out, 'Go on, Bob, hey, Sophie, out you go, scoot !' The lambs baaa-ed, tumbled and skipped out of the door into the field with their mothers.

Jock watched with a hard eye.

'And of course, ye'd never name a farm animal, would ye?'

'Oh no.' Geordie replied, conscious how amateurish he must have appeared to the veteran sheep producer with a medal.

'Ye never name a farm animal. Then they become pets. Then they become part of the family. Then ye eat them and then ye become a cannibal.'

'Interesting point of view.' Geordie marvelled at Jock's logic.

'Aye, but true.'

As it happened, Geordie did have a favourite lamb. Bob held his own with the other lambs, but was smaller and more delicate than his peers. Geordie loved his tight white curls and jet black eyes. Bob always ran up when he appeared in the field with the feed bucket, and followed him around on his sheeply chores. Geordie would sometimes pick up Bob on some important pretext of lamb husbandry, but really just to give him a hug and a pat. He would then put him down gently by a low trough to give him first dibs at the food.

One morning Bob was not in the general hubbub of the hungry flock as Geordie entered the field. He put feed out in the troughs, then looked around for his wee friend. At the far end of the field he spotted a pair of buzzards fussing over something on the ground. He walked over. Bob's eyes had been pecked out, his innards scattered and partly consumed.

'F*****g buzzards! ' he shouted. 'I'll get you later.' He picked up the mauled carcass and buried Bob under a rhododendron with a silent prayer.

'Ye'd never name a farm animal, would ye?' he muttered furiously as he headed for the gun room.

It became a wet, warm Spring. Josie noticed two ewes and three lambs limping one afternoon. By the following morning more than half the animals were limping. The vet diagnosed foot rot and prescribed penicillin.

'How do they take the penicillin?'

'All they need is one injection in the fold of skin at the back of their necks.'

'Ah yes,' Josie replied distractedly, 'silly me.'

'You'll have to repeat the treatment whenever the problem recurs.' The vet went on, adding, 'It's a common problem with Bowmonts. They're lovely sheep but very susceptible to damp.'

'I thought that breeding Merinos with Shetlands was supposed to eliminate that?'

'Not quite.'

The health cure took most of the following morning. The limping sheep were bunched into a gated pen, queuing patiently as they were narrowed, one by one, into a footbath. At the end of the footbath was a contraption which trapped each animal in a narrow gated corridor.

This was where Josie grabbed them by the scruff and injected penicillin into the fold of skin in their necks. The gate was opened, each sheep hobbled back into the field and resumed grazing.

The wet, warm Spring slid into a wet, warm Summer. The limping had ceased, the foot rot was under control and the lambs were growing chubby. One evening Josie and Geordie sipped their gin and tonics as they leaned on the gate. They liked to admire their flock as it grazed peacefully.

At that moment of well-earned satisfaction, Jock's Land Rover came bouncing along the track.

'Hello, glad to see ye this evening. I came round earlier but ye were out.' Jock shouted from the driver's window.

'Anything we can help you with?' Geordie replied.

'No, but ye might want to check your animals for blow fly.'

'Blow fly? What's that?' Josie queried.

'A rather nasty infection. Bluebottles lay their eggs on the rear end of the sheep and the maggots bury themselves into the soft tissue. They will literally eat your animal from inside.'

'Charming. What do you look for?' Geordie enquired.

'See that ewe over there? She looks uncomfortable, trying to bite at the wool on her haunch. Her tail is flicking furiously and she's not feeding. Probably got blow fly.'

Josie was close to tears. 'How can we find out for sure?'

'Come on, I'll show you.' Jock turned off the engine, got out of the Land Rover and released his collie. They walked across the field and surrounded the afflicted sheep, which didn't run from them. Jock grabbed the animal and turned her upside down. 'See here. A blow fly strike in the breech area. Fortunately it hasn't developed too far.' The wound seethed with maggots. Geordie nearly gagged.

'What happens is that the bluebottle—Calliphora SPP—is attracted to wet wool, particularly if immersed in urine or faeces. It lays eggs in these places, which develop into maggots. The maggots burrow into the sheep, causing severe irritation and toxaemia. This is known as a "strike".'

Jock pulled a lethal-looking pair of shears from his belt. He delicately cut the wool away from the infection and dabbed it with yellow liquid from a plastic bottle. The maggots fell away and Geordie stubbed them into the ground. Jock held up the bottle:

'Organophosphates are the most effective way to treat or prevent strikes.' He looked around the field. 'I see a couple of other candidates. Ye're probably going to have to dip all of these sheep before long.'

'Where do we dip them? We don't have the facilities here.'

'Ye can find mobile dipping contractors through the local Machinery Ring. Your problem is that ye hardly have enough sheep to make it worthwhile. It will be very expensive per sheep.' Jock said, adding, 'Coming to think of it I'm having my sheep dipped next week. If you get your sheep to Nether Kinmont on Tuesday morning, I can stick them through the dip with mine.'

Josie looked over at Geordie, who nodded. 'That's very kind. We'll do that.'

Nether Kinmont was three miles away and they were able to borrow a trailer for the morning. The dipping was under way by the time they arrived at 7.30 and their sheep were duly added to the queue for baptism in the chemical solution.

Half way through the morning Jock was called away to a meeting. 'Don't worry about me: load up your sheep once they've had a chance to dry out and we'll catch up later in the week.'

At first, Josie's flock stayed in a tight bunch after dipping, but as more and more sheep from Jock's flock came through the tank, the two flocks intermingled and grazed together. The lambs from each flock cavorted and ran around the field in mixed groups. Very soon it became exceedingly difficult to make out the Bowmonts among Jock's Shetlands and Suffolks, and quite impossible to distinguish the lambs.

'Shit, how do we untangle this?' Geordie growled. The dip contractors were visitors to the area and couldn't help. It was decided to leave the Bowmonts in the field and catch up with Jock later.

They returned to the farm with an empty trailer. They didn't talk much. The field was curiously quiet when they got back.

'You're not going to believe this...' Josie began her phone conversation with Jock.

They planned to meet on Jock's hillside the following morning at 9 o'clock.

'Your 22 sheep are hopelessly entangled with my 300 sheep. So what would you do?' Jock asked them in the morning. Geordie felt like a rookie at the first year oral exams at veterinary college.

'I think your dog might be the solution.' ventured Geordie.

'All right, I'll let the dog out and you tell him what to do.' Jock opened the tailgate of the Land Rover. The collie jumped out and sat at his feet. 'All right -you tell him.'

'Good boy, fetch.' Geordie made a sweeping arc towards the field with his arm. The dog cocked his head in incomprehension. 'Go on, find Josie's sheep.'

Jock's face was one huge grin. The dog looked up quizzically at his master for guidance. Jock shouted a few words in guttural Scots. The dog ran towards a group of sheep grazing on a knoll 300 yards away. Jock whistled twice. The dog disappeared momentarily behind the knoll and reappeared, herding a group of 13 sheep. He steered them to within 25 yards of Josie, where they remained. Jock whistled again: two long, low blasts rising to a high-pitched peep peep. The dog ran towards a dip in the ground and came out chasing five lambs, then rounded up the four remaining singletons before herding them together to join the original 13 standing near Josie. The entire exercise had taken under 10 minutes.

'There's your 22 sheep. Where d'you want them?' Jock asked.

'In the open van please.'

'Well I'll be damned,' Geordie mused as they drove home with a van full of bleating wool. 'It's amazing how that dog knows exactly which sheep to single out.'

Josie filled out the requisite forms and put them on file. Her sheep had been dipped in a chemical called diazinon, which had a meat withdrawal period of 70 days. That is to say, their meat was chemically unfit for consumption for 70 days after the sheep were dipped. Not that eating her precious flock was ever an option, but it troubled Josie that her organic sheep were being exposed to such powerful chemicals.

Organic animals were not supposed to be treated with certain chemicals or drugs, unless it was a last resort matter of animal welfare. Her dilemma was that the Bowmonts were susceptible to ailments that needed to be treated with these chemicals, so they shouldn't honestly be called organic, in her opinion.

73

Geordie was on the way to the field carrying his usual two buckets of treats. Josie walked beside him, uncharacteristically pensive.

'I love the way they all come running when they see us appear round the corner.' Geordie scattered treats just inside the gate. Although their lambs were fully grown, the ewes always let them have first pickings.

Then Josie delivered her thunderbolt.

'Geordie, I think we're going to have to sell the sheep.'

'You must be joking. They're part of the family now.' Two ewes jostled for oat biscuits he held in his open hand. Their woolly muzzles vacuumed up the treats, which then crunched satisfyingly. He was dumbstruck.

'Trouble is that we live too far north for Bowmonts to live successfully on an organic farm. Unless we give them chemicals and drugs they'll fall ill. They're not sustainable in this climate.'

'Sustainable, shmustainable, who cares? They're happy and loved here.'

'Maybe so, but the whole business plan depends on organic, healthy animals.'

'So what are you going to do?' Geordie was devastated. He chucked the remaining treats to the ground and closed the gate.

'Send them to market.'

'We can't just send them to market. They'll end up at the knackers.'

'Well, we can stipulate that they sell as breeding stock rather than for meat.'

The executive from the Auction Mart was not the callous, rough-handed, bloody-aproned meat-processor in a white van they'd expected. The well-dressed young man arrived at the front door in a BMW. He was well-spoken and educated. He admired the way they'd nurtured the flock and agreed wholeheartedly that it had to stay together.

'They're such beautiful animals. I don't think we should put them into auction up here. I'll make enquiries with our associates in the south and find out if any English farmers might be interested in them. Leave it with me.'

Two weeks later the young man called. 'I've found a home for your sheep. There's an organic farmer just outside Totnes in Devon who's interested in Bowmonts. He'll take the whole flock.' The young man stated a price. It was a hefty loss compared to the investment they'd made in the project.

'At least they'll stay together and someone else can build on the work we've done.' Josie unconvincingly tried to sound cheerful.

'Yeah, if you say so.'

There was a great deal of indignant baaa-ing when the sheep were rounded up. Geordie handed out treats to attract them towards the vehicle. The last ewe to be chased up the ramp was Bob's mother. He'd called her Vanessa. She was easily recognizable because her left ear pointed downwards and her head was always at a tilt- maybe the result of an encounter with a dog or rough handling when she was a lamb. Vanessa looked back and stared hard at Geordie. The driver gave her a push and slammed the door behind her. The ramp closed.

As the truck drove off, Geordie gave the bucket a mighty kick and scattered sheep treats across the field.

'Don't do that, Honey. They're off to a healthier life.'

'I feel like Judas Iscariot.'

Three months later they decided to take a break and visit London for a few days. After seeing a show in the West End one evening they strolled through Covent Garden.

'It's brilliant being able to take the time to wander around and not be beholden to anyone or anything. Look at that fire-eater!' Josie exclaimed excitedly. Every few yards along the street there was a different act: sword-swallowers, mime artists, card sharps, old-

fashioned buskers, acrobats, comedians and miscellaneous shysters.
'Yes, I enjoy the freedom of being away from Balnadarg too.
What do you feel like for dinner?'

'Something simple and wholesome.'

'How about that: Le Perroquet Organique? ' He pointed at a
bustling restaurant with tables set out on the pavement.

'Yeah, looks great to me. Their customers seem happy enough.'
she said, pointing at the diners outside.

They sat at a table and studied the menu. Josie ordered sole
meuniere and Geordie chose filet d'agneau. They also ordered two
demi carafes, one of house red, one of house white.

'Nice bohemian atmosphere here.' Josie stretched across the table
and held Geordie's hand. 'I'm so glad we came away for a few days.'
A man was reciting poetry by Baudelaire to a group of students at
the table next to theirs.

The wine arrived. 'Cheers. Here's to the dear old Bowmonts.'
Geordie lifted his glass to Josie.

'And to dear old you.' Josie laughed. 'Or should I say, dear old
ewe.'

'I wonder what they're up to?' he mused, having missed the pun.

'Oh, probably doing the Milan fashion circuit with their wool.'

'I miss Vanessa, with her floppy ear.'

'She'll be charming a new audience, no doubt.'

'Yeah, suppose so.' he replied wistfully, sipping his wine and
changing the subject.

'Mmm,' Geordie held his glass to the light, 'this is not a wine
that flatters straight from the glass.'

'Pompous twit.' Josie teased her husband.

Their meals arrived. They were beautifully presented, consisting
of simple French provincial cuisine.

The waiter came by. 'Is everything to your satisfaction madame,
monsieur?'

'Excellent.' Geordie replied enthusiastically. Then remembering
the menu's claim that all the restaurant's meat was sourced

organically, asked, 'As a matter of interest, where did this delicious filet d'agneau come from?'

'I'll find out and let you know, monsieur.'

They finished the meal and sat back contentedly sipping the last of the wine. The waiter returned.

'I asked the chef and he tells me that he purchases all his lamb from a small organic farm outside Totnes in Devon. They are the best producers in England.'

The carafe of cheap white wine had worked its magic. Josie planted a kiss on Geordie's shocked lips as he began to mumble, 'How do I know ...'

'Don't go there, darlin', but I'm sure that Vanessa wouldn't have wanted to be eaten by anyone else.'

The Percy Arms

'One of the defining moments of modern literature,' Geordie announced authoritatively, 'was Marcel Proust's revelation of the memories that flooded back when he sank his teeth into that tea-soaked madeleine.'

Andrew rolled his eyes. 'You're such a bloody pseud, Geordie. Why can't you make a point without bringing Proust into it?' He stuffed a handful of peanuts into his mouth and swilled back a mouthful of lager.

'I shall choose to ignore that comment. As everyone knows, a madeleine is "one of those squat, plump little cakes...which look as if they had been moulded in the fluted valve of a scallop shell". You can still buy them today in practically any *pâtisserie* in France.'

'So what revelation have you had lately that will transform modern literature?' Andrew placed his empty glass firmly on the table, crossed his arms and gave Geordie an amused look.

'I don't have any particular revelations.' Geordie waved his hand dismissively. 'But I was driving through Northumberland the other day. I stopped at the Percy Arms in Otterburn for lunch, which turned out to be a bit of a madeleine moment for me. Remember that place?'

'Can't say that I do.' Andrew pursed his lips and shook his head. 'Jog my memory.'

'Hitch hiking to London from Invernorth when we were teenagers? Ring a bell?'

'Can't say it does. A hell of a lot's happened in my life since then. I vaguely remember a disastrous jape when I caught pneumonia in a field somewhere. Was that with you?'

'That was with me.' Geordie smiled. But realising that the episode was otherwise buried, if not erased from his friend's memory, he dropped it. 'Never mind, it's completely inconsequential. Changing the subject, how's your mother? Is she still alive?'

'She passed away two years ago. It was a blessing, really:

'I'm so sorry to hear that.'

'In her last years it was as if she was waiting for someone to arrive and square the circle. Her last words were, "He's never going to come back, is he? I think it's best if I just go now."'

'I wish I was eighteen again.' Andrew's mother remarked wistfully. She sat on the bed watching her son and Geordie preparing to leave the house. Very shortly, they would leave and walk to the end of the drive, stick out their thumbs and hitch-hike to London. Such freedom was almost inconceivable to her.

Geordie had been staying at Invernorth for much of the summer and had become intoxicated by his best friend's mother. She was incredibly alluring to his teenage eye. Her curves, her legs, the way she moved, dazzled him. She was now inflaming Geordie's fantasy by wishing she was eighteen. What was she *really* saying?

He was too inexperienced to understand the game. She had flattered him quietly all summer, comparing him variously to the youth in *Death in Venice,* Donatello's *David* and the pretty boy in *Fellini Satyricon.* He was coy and restrained, though his fantasies were far from innocent. He was simply too young to know how to reach for what he, and for all he knew, the lovely Lady Invernorth, desired.

Andrew's father was a bluff aristocrat who lived for his cigar, port and coffee after dinner each day to anaesthetize his disappointments. He was a kind and generous soul but was knackered and crotchety by 10 o'clock in the evening.

Geordie looked up in surprise as he tightened the straps on his green canvas knapsack, the only baggage he ever carried. 'Yes, it would be great fun if you were eighteen.' This was his only expression of interest to the woman who had ravaged his imagination for the past six weeks.

'Thank you very much for having me to stay.' He stood up and looked into her face. 'I've really enjoyed myself.' Geordie shook her hand. He was to be haunted for many years by the way her hand had lingered in his, by the moistness of her lips, by the fire in her green eyes but most of all, by her parting words: 'I really mean it.'

It was a measure of the boys' optimism that they had decided to hitchhike to London at lunchtime and not thought of leaving Invernorth until 3pm. They'd given no consideration to the privations of the route, or that they might not reach London, a mere 400 miles away, by nightfall.

Their first ride weaved around farm roads and deposited the boys a few miles away on the A68 in Jedburgh. They had to walk a long way out of town before finding a safe spot to stand, stick out their thumbs and continue hitching for a ride. Eventually a Land Rover pulled up, only to deposit them on a remote farm track ten miles on. The boys walked a mile back to the main road and were picked up immediately by an army officer in a hurry.

'Going to Redesdale. Any help to you?'

'That's great.' Andrew enthused.

Neither boy had a clue where Redesdale was, but it was south, and south was good.

'OK, hop in lads.'

They bombed along the A68 and soon crossed the English border into Northumberland. Then, as now, there was little traffic on the road. The evening sunshine slanted across the moorland in a glorious spectacle of soft golden light. Geordie felt elated. He was always happiest when he was on the move. It thrilled him that nobody in the world knew where he was, except Andrew of course, as they raced across the historic Border landscape.

'We'll be at Redesdale Camp in a few minutes,' the officer announced. 'Listen boys, I'm in good time. Why don't I take you down to Otterburn and leave you at the Percy Arms? You'll have a better chance of getting a ride from there.'

'That would be very kind.' Andrew replied.

'Yes, thank you very much.' Geordie nodded.

The bar in the Percy Arms radiated eternal Englishness, with its buzz of local chatter, tobacco smoke, laughter and the clink of glassware from a cheerful barmaid as she pulled pints.

'What do you want to drink?' Andrew asked.

'A pint of Starbright.' Geordie replied, adding anxiously, 'You know, it's past 7 o'clock and it's taken us all this time to travel about 60 miles. What do you think we should do from here?'

'We need a couple of drinks to take stock'. Andrew responded firmly.

They sat at a table on a terrace in the sunshine, feeling steadily more carefree as they imbibed the potent Newcastle brew. Geordie walked back to the bar to fetch another round. When he returned to the table, Andrew was in conversation with a middle-aged couple sitting nearby.

'Dotty and Richard can take us to Ponteland,' Andrew announced exultantly.

'That's extremely kind of you,' Geordie thanked the couple as he placed the beers on the table.

'No problem, luddy. If you can give us 'alf an hour for us to 'ave a bite, we'll take you right to the junction of the A1 at Gosforth. One truck to London from thur and yer in business.'

The boys sank their beers.

'Come on, Andrew, let's explore this place.' They agreed to meet Dotty and Richard in the car park in 30 minutes, shouldered their packs and wandered out of the Percy Arms. Close by, a tumbling stream burbled under a bridge. The boys kicked off their shoes, slid down the bank and paddled in the clear, fast water.

'Man, this feels good.' Geordie exclaimed.

'Yep, bloody fantastic.' Andrew paused. 'I need a pee.'

'Now you mention it …'

They scrambled up the bank and stood in a grove of twisted apple trees in an ancient orchard. The evening sun slanted behind them, warming the back of their legs and casting long shadows through the trees. There was not a breath of wind; a cloud of gnats rose and fell above a pungent clump of wild garlic in the orchard.

'"In a wailful choir the small gnats mourn…borne aloft or sinking as the light wind sinks or dies." D'you like Keats?' Andrew looked across at Geordie as he relieved himself.

'Quite like Keats. Prefer Baudelaire, though,' he replied precociously.

'Mmm. You know, Geordie, if this moment could be transposed for eternity, I would be happy to die right now. I simply can't imagine a happier moment in my life.'

'Mmm.' Geordie's back muscles quivered like a thoroughbred hunter in the sunshine as his bladder emptied.

Dotty and Richard were standing beside their car when the boys returned. True to his word, Richard deposited them an hour later on the southbound ramp of the A1 at Gosforth.

'This is very grown-up.' Geordie observed as lorries thundered past and successive white Ford builders' vans raced by. Private car drivers were too intimidated to slow down for hitch hikers at this fast and busy intersection.

'Nobody's going to stop here.' Andrew concluded. 'I spotted a lay-by about half a mile back. Perhaps we should go back there and nobble any driver who slips in for a fag or a pee.'

'*Reculer pour mieux avancer.*' Geordie replied.

'Good Lord, French A level really has made you truly insufferable.'

They hung around the lay-by for two hours. The evening had become dark and damp. They were hungry, tired and dispirited. Boldly, they had gone up to dozens of drivers to ask for a lift. Their response had varied from the traditional North Country 'Fook aff' to the more namby pamby 'Well, I would, but…'

'Looks like we may have to spend the night in this godforsaken place.' Geordie concluded at about 11 o'clock.

'I really wasn't expecting this.' Andrew shivered in the light velvet jacket he'd brought to look cool in London. 'I need a drink.'

At that moment a scruffy decorator's pick-up truck pulled into the lay-by. Ladders and other paraphernalia of his trade were strapped to the roof of the vehicle. The driver left the door open and the engine running as he took three purposeful paces from the vehicle and peed,

horse-like, on the grass. Andrew shouted to him:
'Any chance of a lift going south?'
'Aye. Can take you to Doncaster, but we've got to get a move on.'
The boys threw their kit in the rear and crammed into the front of the pick-up. The driver was a jolly fellow and deposited them, some three hours later, at a transport café on the A1 just north of Doncaster.
'You can't just sit 'ere all night long, you know.' The waitress shooed the boys out after they'd lingered for an hour over mugs of coffee and had tried to put their heads down on the plastic-topped table.
There was a paddock behind the transport café. Geordie took the spare clothes out of his knapsack and bundled himself up like a Michelin man. He found a dry hollow in a hedge, curled up and slept fitfully for a few hours. Andrew sat upright nearby, kept awake by the incessant rumble of traffic on the A1, chain-smoking Sullivan Powells, coughing and moaning loudly about how 'everything had gone horribly wrong.'
At first light the boys made their way back to the café, where mercifully their waitress had changed shift. They washed off the grime at an oily basin in the men's lavatory and ate a hot breakfast.
'I have to say, old man, I was reflecting last night that this isn't my scene at all.' Andrew stirred his coffee, avoiding eye contact with Geordie; his fag smoked in a tin ashtray on the table.
'It's not exactly my idea of heaven either, but we're over the worst. It's a fine summer day and we could be in London in four hours with a following wind.'
'That's as may be, but I'm done with this caper, Geordie. I'm going to call a cab to get me to the station and take the train to London from Doncaster. Want to come?'
'Absolutely not. We've come this far and the rest is easy.' Geordie was truly disappointed by his friend's cop-out. 'Come on, you've got to be able to say you hitched the entire distance.'

'What's the point? Spending the night in a damp field in Yorkshire has done me in.'

Geordie was picked up by a fish lorry from Berwick leaving the car park before Andrew's cab had arrived from Doncaster. As the boys parted he shouted, 'See you in Cavendish Square, 6.00pm this evening for drinks.'

His last lift was from a companionable sales rep in a Jaguar who left him outside Chesham Tube station at 11.30. By 4 o'clock Geordie had taken a bath and was awake after a luxurious nap in his aunt's commodious flat; by early evening he was raring for London life.

It was 7.00pm and still no sign of Andrew. He was an hour late. Geordie sat in a deep armchair contemplating his third Glenmorangie, wondering how to play the next step. Should he call Invernorth, nonchalantly asking for Andrew's whereabouts? Problem was that his parents would immediately get the wind-up, because Geordie was supposedly Andrew's best friend. It might be difficult to explain that he had lost their son at a transport café near Doncaster that morning.

On the other hand, Andrew was supposed to be staying with him at Cavendish Square. Andrew had other London friends, for sure. Geordie wondered if he'd turned up at the door while he'd been napping that afternoon. Andrew would have hung around for an hour or so and decided to doss down elsewhere. That is exactly what Geordie would have done; he would never leave his night's sleeping arrangements to chance. Not in London, at any rate.

'Only one way to find out.' Geordie walked over to the telephone and dialled the familiar number at Invernorth. He wobbled unsteadily as the phone rang and rang. He could picture so clearly the handset resonating in the cavernous oak-panelled hall; he could hear the footsteps on the parquet and the connecting doors slamming, the dogs barking and someone shouting, 'I'll get it.' It always took ten or more rings before anyone picked up the phone at Invernorth. Unless someone happened to be walking past at the time, which they never were.

'Selkirk 748, good evening.' She had picked up the phone. Geordie was momentarily fazed but quickly recovered.

'Gut evenink, pliz might ah spik to Andrew? Pliz.' Geordie mimicked an imaginary Central European accent in a low, gruff voice.

'I beg your pardon?'

'Pliz might ah spik to Andrew? Pliz.' he repeated.

'This isn't Geordie, is it?' Lady Invernorth sounded oddly hopeful. He couldn't possibly show his hand now. This would give him another reason to kick himself in future years.

'Me no Geordie, me Boris. I-am-a-school-friend-of-Andrew.' He articulated each word as only a foreigner would do.

'Will Andrew know what this is about?'

'I am Boris, his school friend. No agenda, just want to talk.' Please just tell me that Andrew's at home.

'Just wait a moment please, Geordie.' She laughed. She'd rumbled him. Oh, her sweet voice.

At least ten minutes passed, during which Geordie could hear the aforementioned comings and goings. Doors opened and slammed, voices ebbed and flowed, a dog yapped, footsteps crossed the hall. He thought he had been forgotten, when finally the footsteps got increasingly louder as someone approached and picked up the phone.

'Yes? This is Andrew here.' He sounded congested and his voice had dropped a few octaves.

'You wanker!'

'Geordie! Have you any idea how sick I am? I have pneumonia.'

'Sorry to hear it, mate, but you might have called to let me know where you were.'

'I got to Doncaster station. I was feeling really rough, called my parents. They told me to return north; picked me up at Berwick a few hours later. Doctor says I have caught pneumonia.'

'Sorry to hear that, but you should have called to say what you were doing.'

'Yeah, sorry mate. Well I'm off games for another fortnight, maybe longer.'

That blew their long-planned voyage of discovery to London and the French Riviera.

Thin clouds scudded across a full moon as the friends left the Edinburgh New Town bar. Andrew had downed at least three beers for every one that Geordie had consumed. In his rubber-limbed condition Andrew used the cast iron Georgian railings for support to make his way along the street. At regular intervals there were gates in the railings which opened onto stone staircases leading down to basement courtyards.

In the midst of his inane chatter, Andrew pushed on a gate and suddenly disappeared. A fearful clatter ensued as he tumbled headlong into the gloom. A string of rich oaths came up from the blackness. Geordie cracked up with laughter.

'Are you all right?'

'Buggered if I know.'

'Have you broken anything?'

'About six flowerpots.'

More uncontrolled mirth.

'No—your limbs, you idiot. Did you break anything?'

'Well, I can't get up, if that's what you mean. My leg's bent under me at a funny angle.'

Geordie descended into the gloom. It was hard to see much, but he could tell straight away in the faint street lighting that Andrew was in trouble.

'Just as well you're too drunk to feel much pain.'

'If I wasn't drunk I wouldn't be here.'

More helpless laughter.

'I think we'd better call for help. Don't move. I'll be back in 5 minutes.'

The barman whose services they'd used all evening made a quick call. Within 10 minutes an ambulance was on the scene. The paramedics rapidly diagnosed a compound fracture, injected copious morphine and packaged Andrew onto a stretcher. It took the muscle of three men to haul him out of the basement.

As Andrew was being lifted into the ambulance, he slurred,

'A few years ago, Jean Paul Sartre was hit by a taxi in Paris. His last words before he passed out were, "Thank God something's happened at last." Couldn't have said it better myself, old man.'

Andrew grinned triumphantly; his eyes closed as the morphine finally overwhelmed him.

Geordie would have loved to point out that Sartre was an atheist, but never mind. He accompanied Andrew to the A&E unit and sat by his comatose friend until the duty nurse confirmed he'd be kept in overnight.

He walked home through the hospital car park and along a tree lined-road. The moon shone brightly through the branches. Contrasting the evening's squalid drunkenness with that distant summer afternoon, he pictured Andrew's mother with vivid clarity and quietly intoned Poe's famous lines:

"For the moon never beams without bringing me dreams ...of the beautiful Annabel Lee."

The Family Seat

As Geordie was engrossed in the daily newspaper he only partially registered that Josie had entered the room and taken her place on the sofa.

She picked up an auctioneer's catalogue entitled "The Dispersal of Lord Taykirk's Effects" that was lying on the coffee table, and began to leaf through.

'They've got a Vuillamy long case clock with a reserve price of £25,000.'

'Yeah?'

'Yeah.'

'Why don't we get two?' sarcasm was guaranteed when Geordie was interrupted doing something that required concentration, like reading the sports pages of the Express.

'Not what I'm looking for,' She continued leafing.

'Here's an early 18th century Quaich, a Scottish drinking cup. Its metal bound body is divided into fourteen alternating yew and ebony sections with an engraved silver metal boss and its two lugs mounted with silver.'

'Well I never. Want it?'

'Nope.'

'Hey Geordie. Here's an oil painting by William Carrick.'

'What's the subject?'

'The Kingussie Highland Games, circa 1957.'

Geordie looked over his spectacles as Josie showed him the painting. It depicted a large circular gathering of spectators in a field beside the Spey. Pennants fluttered off marquees, an ex- army ambulance was parked nearby, green hills framed the scene; white clouds scudded overhead. The painting radiated lightness and optimism, like so many of Carrick's works.

'I can almost feel the occasion,' Geordie observed. 'You know, my grandfather was a great pal of Bill Carrick's. They used to meet in the Gordon Arms for a drink on Saturday mornings. And Sunday evenings, and Monday lunch, and Tuesday afternoons, coming to think of it ... until they both ended upside down in a ditch one day in Grandfather's Alvis. My grandmother forbade further social gatherings with Carrick after that. He was an excellent painter, though. What's the estimated price on that one? '

'£3,000 to £4,000.'

'Pass.'

Josie continued to exclaim and coo as she thumbed through the catalogue to the mms and wows of her husband.

'Aah, here's something we need.' Was this the Eureka moment?

'Yeah?'

'Yeah. A chair for the hall. We've always needed the right chair for that corner. Here, this one's perfect.' She folded back the page and showed Geordie a photograph of the main entrance of Taykirk Castle. Six un-matching, but curiously harmonious oak chairs were scattered around the perimeter of the hall.

'So which one do you like?'

'This one—it's the only one which would fit in our hall.' She made a slightly contemptuous sweeping gesture across the photograph, as if to say it was completely obvious which chair was the right one.

'Yes, I see. It is a lovely chair, isn't it? What's the expected price range?'

'£500 to £750.'

'Sounds like an expensive place to park your arse.'

'Don't be ridiculous. There are chairs for sitting and chairs for showing. Everyone knows that.'

'So, do you want it?'

'Yeah... but not particularly.' This was Josie's way of saying she'd love to have it but didn't want to raise her expectations.

'I'm glad you said that.'

Josie continued leafing. 'Here's an amazing porcelain Qianlong dinner service. It was commissioned by the family when they were involved in the East India Company in the late 18th century. Can you imagine the dinner party conversations these plates have witnessed over the past 200 years?'

Before Geordie could enthuse, she looked at her watch. 'Oops, I've got to get ready for a consultation in 10 minutes. See you later.' She left the catalogue on the table and dashed out of the room.

Geordie waited a minute, put down the sports pages, leaned over and picked up the catalogue. He turned to the furniture section. Not one, but three pages of chairs had been photographed in the hall of Taykirk Castle.

Which was the one she liked? She'd specifically said she liked the oak one. Not very helpful; they were all oak, apart from three mahogany and two yew chairs. She'd said the expected price range was £500 to £700. This narrowed his choice to seven chairs sporting an expected range of £500 to £700.

'Which is the only one that would fit our hall?' Geordie asked himself. He got up and walked through to the hall. It was a light space with cream walls and light curtains. The sofa was cream, two wing armchairs were upholstered in pale blue; the carpet was a predominantly light green tartan. The overall effect was feminine, light and airy. 'That rules out these ones.' Geordie blanked out four heavy oak baronial armchairs. None of the final three chairs could be said to have been feminine. He climbed the stairs to look down on the hall, to see where she might wish to put another chair. He then tried to imagine her taste in oak chairs.

The choice narrowed down to a pale oak Rennie Mackintosh ladder-back art nouveau chair, and what the catalogue described as "An early 18th century Scottish oak caqueteuse armchair."

'Blimey, what is on earth is a caqueteuse? Must be one of those pretentious terms used by auction houses to baffle the public, like finial, spadroon and torchere.' He reached for the Oxford English Dictionary. No word was listed between capybara and car. He turned to a nearby dusty French dictionary.

'Aha! We have two definitions—a gossip who chatters

ceaselessly without discretion. I can think of a few who'd fit that bill. Or, an old-fashioned low chair with a high straight back. Mm. Which is the right one, I wonder?'

The trick was to establish which of the two chairs Josie had in mind without hinting that he intended to bid and give it for her birthday. That was surely why she'd so pointedly leafed through the catalogue, Geordie figured.

Over the following week, completely out of context, Geordie turned to Josie and asked questions like, 'If you had the choice between an old-fashioned dark furniture house, or a light and airy modern house, which would you go for?'

'I like to mix and match. It can look great to have good pieces of old furniture in a modern house.'

Great! Geordie had his answer.

'But I also really like very old houses where the owners are not stuck in a rut and are open to good quality modern pieces.'

'Oh. Yes, I agree. There's a lot to be said for either view.' He was no further on.

The day of the auction arrived. Geordie had run out of subterfuges for extracting Josie's preference without giving the game away. He would just have to take a view and go for it. He reckoned they were both fabulous chairs, if you liked that sort of thing, and nobody could fail to be thrilled to receive either of them as a default birthday present, surely? As he slipped out of the house after breakfast, Josie called:

'Where are you going, Honey?'

'I've got various meetings on farm business this morning. I won't be back until this afternoon.'

A large marquee had been set up on the front lawn of Taykirk Castle. It was a warm, sunny day; the canvas sides had been rolled up to let in the breeze. Thirty rows of plastic chairs, twenty wide, had been set out to accommodate the mishmash of dealers, investors, socialites, punters and voyeurs wanting to be in at the kill at dear old Lord Taykirk's estate. Speakers had been placed at the front, middle and back of the tent so that everyone could hear what was going on. Geordie's chairs were lot numbers 185 and 188. Rennie Mack was 185 and Caquette was 188. They wouldn't be coming up for two hours, but he wanted to sit all the way through to gauge the spending power of the crowd. Who knows, there might be an opportunity to pick up a spadroon or an ormolu furniture mount that had fallen between the cracks. He'd seen it before, when items of considerable value had been overlooked and sold for a clearance price at auctions.

'My Lords, Ladies and Gentlemen,' The auctioneer began, 'Welcome to Taykirk Castle on this lovely Highland day. We have been instructed by the family and heirs of Lord Taykirk to sell a large number of effects, so without further ado, I'd like to start with Lot no 1, A pair of Continental silver Pricket candlesticks. I have a bid of £500.'

A hand flickered. The estimated sale price range in the catalogue was £400 to £600.

'£550. I have a bid of £600.'

The hand flickered again.

'£650. I have a bid of £700.'

The dealer nodded .

'£750. I have £800.'

Another nod.

'£900. I have £1,000.'

The hapless dealer was drawn all the way up to £2400 until he finally shook his head in exasperation and the Pricket candlesticks went to an anonymous bidder on the Internet.

The auctioneer worked his way through urn-shaped castelettes, bronze figurines, a Victorian elephant's foot, long-case clocks, a rocking horse, a collection of Meissen and fifty lots of Chinese porcelain from the family's East India Company days. The bidding was brisk and there was obviously a lot of firepower in the tent. Geordie was tempted to bid speculatively a couple of times, but held off; he had to keep his powder dry for lots 185 and 188.

'Lot 183. A Georgian Rosewood parlour chair. I have interest at

£600.'

'That's rich,' thought Geordie. 'Catalogue range is £400 to £500.'

A hand went up.

'£650. I have interest at £700.'

Internet interest ran out at £950 but two bidders in the room pushed the price up to £1400.

'Lot 184. An early Victorian oak wing armchair. I'll start the bidding at £150.'

'That's more like it. Catalogue range is £350 to £400.' Geordie thought.

'£150? Any bids? Yes madam. I have £200.'

'£250. The gentleman in the corner.'

'£300'

A hand.

'£350'

A twitch.

'£400'

A nod.

'£500'

So they waved, twitched and nodded to £900. Chairs were obviously hot on this day, which didn't augur well for Geordie.

'Lot 185. An oak ladder-back Art Nouveau chair after Rennie Mackintosh. I'll start the bidding at £200.' The auctioneer scanned the room for a sign of life.

'No bids at £200, who'll bid me £100?'

A hand.

'I have a bid for £150. Who'll bid me £200?'

Another hand.

Geordie was relieved. It looked like the bidding was going to take off, so he'd hang back for the second chair. Before he knew it, however, the gavel came down and the Rennie Mackintosh chair sold for £250.

'Bloody hell, I should have got it while I had the chance. I'll have to get the next one.' He'd become flustered and sweaty. Lots 185, 186 and 187 each went for considerably more than their expected ranges. His heart was pounding.

'Lot 188. An early 18th Century Scottish oak caqueteuse armchair. I have a lot of interest here. I can start the bidding at £1,000.' £1,000! Geordie almost died.

'£1,100.'

A girl nodded. She was on the phone to a client.

'£1,200.'

Geordie did not bid. Many nods, waves, twitches and disappointed head shakes later, the auctioneer summarized,

'We're standing at £5,500. Fair warning, we're going at £5,500 for this 18th Century Scottish oak caqueteuse.' As the auctioneer lifted the gavel to conclude the bidding, Geordie panicked. His hand shot up, as if in a nightmare.

'Ah! We have a new bidder from the floor. I'm bid £6,000 by the gentleman on my left'.

A murmur rose from the crowd. At least 200 curious faces turned to see Geordie.

'Any advance on £6,000?'

The girl on the phone re-engaged in a heated conversation. Finally, she nodded.

'We have £6,500.'

The crowd whooped.

'Oh fuck it,' Geordie flicked his hand as nonchalantly as a prisoner heading to his execution. He was being watched by everyone in the marquee. His virility was at stake.

'SEVEN THOUSAND POUNDS. We have seven thousand pounds.' The auctioneer turned towards the girl on the phone.

'Any advance on £7,000?'

There was a further lively discussion. The auctioneer must inadvertently have had his microphone pointed in the direction of the girl, because one of her comments came out loud and clear: 'This guy's a nut. He'll pay anything for that chair.' People in the crowd laughed. Geordie sat dispassionately. He may have looked cool, but he was boiling in a stew of adrenalin, absolutely determined to see this bloody chair through to the end.

The girl shook her head, the gavel came down and the crowd roared its approval. Geordie had won ownership of an early 18th century Scottish oak caqueteuse armchair for £7,000, plus the buyer's premium and Value Added Tax—a total of £9,100.

The hubbub died down and the auction moved on to new lots. After a few minutes Geordie surreptitiously slipped out of the marquee and walked into the castle gardens. He sat on a stone bench facing a sundial. He was shaking. He felt sick and more stupid than he'd ever felt before. £9,100 for a chair! What an unbelievable fool he was.

As he mused on his massive stupidity, a voice broke the silence.

'Mind if I join you? I followed you here because I wanted to congratulate you on your purchase'. A distinguished middle-aged man wearing yellow corduroys, well-polished brown brogues, white shirt, spotted red silk tie and a tweed jacket sat beside Geordie on the bench.

'I assume you realize that you've done incredibly well, otherwise you wouldn't have bid so aggressively. The auctioneers completely misattributed that chair. It's not 18th century at all, but 16th century and it's known to have belonged to Mary Queen of Scots. That's why Sebastian was bidding so fiercely on the phone. But when that girl told him that you were a nut, Sebastian realized you knew all about it too, so decided not to waste his time bidding for something he knew he wouldn't get.'

'So what do you think it's worth?' Geordie attempted to sound cool as shock waves of adrenalin continued to spurt through his body.

'Hard to tell, but you'd get an easy multiple of what you paid. I know for a fact there are museums in America who'd pay handsomely for it. You'd do particularly well if a bidding war was set up properly. Of course, that would depend on getting an export licence.'

'Yes, I had a feeling about that chair; I really appreciate you confirming my hunch.'

'Well, it's always good to see a young chap pulling off a coup in the sale room. I'll leave you now as I've got some lots coming up. Here's my card if you'd ever consider selling that chair, or getting together, er, for any other reason. It was a pleasure to meet you.'

As the man wended his way back through the rose garden Geordie glanced at the card. He'd been talking to Stefan de Forestier, the renowned aesthete, collector, writer, broadcaster and pederast.

Geordie was in shock. He plucked a head of lavender and rubbed it in the palm of his hands, then strolled shakily to the payment desk set up in the hall of Taykirk Castle. He made a brief call to his bank manager, who testily confirmed that he'd make funds available to the auctioneer—'But don't make a habit of this, Mr Kinloch'.

After paying for it, he lifted the richly carved caqueteuse and dumped it into the back of his pickup. It was just an old chair, after all.

Early on the morning of Josie's birthday Geordie brought the chair out of hiding and placed it in the corner of the hall. It looked handsome there, he thought, if slightly incongruous next to the soft cream upholstery of its neighbours. He then sat on the sofa pretending to read, and waited in great anticipation.

'Happy birthday.' He exclaimed as Josie appeared on the staircase. 'Thanks Honey. What are you...' She simultaneously spotted the chair and, before she could stop herself, exclaimed, 'That's completely wrong there.'

'I thought you liked it.'

'Well, I do, Honey,' she backtracked, 'But the Rennie Mackintosh I showed you was more in keeping with what we're trying to do here. Don't you think?'

Somewhat deflated, Geordie retreated to his study. He ferretted about and eventually found the address card.

'Hellao, this is Stefan.'

'Hi, this is Geordie Kinloch. We met at the Taykirk auction a while ago...'

'Oh yes, hellao. Of course I remember. How nice to hear you again. You bought that wonderful chair, didn't you?'

'That's why I'm calling.'

The Ley Line

A walled cemetery straddled the junction where the track split from the Roman road and meandered north into the glens. Here, corpses from the clans were laid to rest in ancient times. They were positioned westwards in the stony earth to face the winter sunsets and to mingle forever with the heathery scents of summer.

The cemetery was a relic of the days when farm carts clip - clopped at a steady pace along the ancient road. After the echo of hooves faded off the weathered stones, silence would return but for the sigh of the wind, the buzz of the bumblebee and the cry of the curlew.

Geordie frequently drove through the crossroads at random hours as he made his daily rounds of Balnadarg. He would have been hard-pressed to say exactly when he first noticed. He just gradually became conscious of a man standing by the gates of the cemetery. Was it one, maybe two, weeks ago? The man was about 30 and always wore the same rough Hessian jacket, ragged trousers and what looked like home-made leather boots. His open honest face was framed by a heavy stubble and a fringe haircut. A lean yellow mongrel lay at his feet or sniffed around nearby. The pair always faced west. They always had an air of waiting for something.

Geordie started to wave as he drove past the fellow. In Scotland it was the custom to wave at people you passed on a rural road. The fellow always waved back. It wasn't a cheery wave accompanied by the inane grin that might signal a village idiot. It was a wave of recognition and familiarity. Geordie nicknamed him Jock. It felt like a solid name, a name which conferred the virtues of trust and industry on the man.

Geordie flew into Edinburgh Airport one evening after a long day in London. Josie met him at the terminal.

'Want me to drive?' he volunteered. She had just driven a hundred and fifty miles to the airport to meet him.

98

'Sure—If you're not too tired.'

They clambered into the car, swept across the Forth Bridge and headed north through the gradually thinning traffic. Two hours later, they reached the crossroads. A northern wind was gusting down from the glens. It was speckling with rain in the darkness. A familiar figure was caught in the sweep of headlights as the car took the corner. Jock stood by the cemetery gate in the Hessian jacket, his yellow dog lay on the ground beside him.

'Hey, there's Jock. What on earth's he doing out at this hour?'

'Who's Jock?' Josie peered into the darkness.

'He's my friend. He's always standing there with his dog when I drive past.'

'I can't see anyone. Where is he?'

'Look, right there. Twenty yards away, by the cemetery wall.'

Geordie hooted the horn. Jock lifted his right arm in recognition.

'I can't see anyone. '

'Look, he's waving.'

Josie looked oddly at Geordie: 'I can't see a thing'.

'Plain as a pikestaff, my love.'

They drove on in silence. Geordie thought that Josie must be as blind as a bat; Josie wondered if Geordie might have gone a whisky too far on the flight from London.

Two weeks later on a Saturday afternoon he was transporting his young daughter Emily with two school-friends to a birthday party. He slowed down at the crossroads. 'Hey, look. There's Jock.'

'Who's Jock, Dad?'

'That's Jock, over there, with his dog.'

'I can't see anyone.'

Geordie waved. Jock waved back. 'Look, there he is.'

The young girls fell silent. Geordie heard whispers and muffled giggles from the rear seats of the car as he waved and drove on.

'Nice joke, Dad.'

Jock was still there when they returned two hours later. Geordie said nothing but double-tooted the horn by way of a greeting. Jock lifted his hand in response.

'Dad, why did you toot the horn?'

'Oh, just parental exuberance, Emily. No other reason.'

He looked back to get a better view of Jock and the dog. He couldn't see them in the mirror. They must have moved out of his line of vision.

Maybe it was the barometric pressure, perhaps the position of the moon, or—who knows?—the forgotten anniversary of an atrocity known only to the castle's ancient stones. There were times when activity from the other side, as it were, was rampant at Balnadarg. Geordie and Josie were accustomed, if not quite immune, to the regular bangs and rustles behind the paneling and on the staircase. They were used to the cry of a non-existent child in the attic, although it was hard to ignore as it built up to an eerie wail. The child's screams always ended in a crash, followed by two sickening thumps and dead silence. Until the next time.

There was no telling what ghastliness had been perpetrated in the mists of history to imprint that sound into Balnadarg's walls. The family had simply learned to live with the periodic disruptions that rattled through the castle, rose to a crescendo and faded away as unaccountably as they arrived.

Josie was working in her study when she heard the familiar scrunch, scrunch of footsteps on gravel. It was a sunny spring afternoon. There was nothing intrinsically sinister about that sound, nothing at all. The only odd thing was that there was no gravel outside her window. Like the dreaded visual aura that heralded a migraine, the sound of footsteps on gravel always signaled a period of turmoil in the castle. A door banged.

Geordie was in a jolly mood as he drove back from the farm show. He enjoyed meeting his friends and learning about the latest agricultural grants for farmers. This year, the government—wearing the cloak of 'Brussels', whatever that meant—was paying farmers'to plant indigenous hedges to enhance wildlife habitat' under EC Directive 52a. Eight years earlier 'Brussels' was shelling out cash to farmers 'to remove hedges to improve field productivity' under EC Directive 17b. Having been paid handsomely for complying with the first directive, he now looked forward to being paid handsomely for complying with the second.

As Geordie slowed the car to take the turn at the crossroads, Jock broke away from the cemetery gate and ran towards him, waving his arms frantically. Geordie stopped and wound down the window.

'I was wondering how long it would be before we met. I must have passed you a hundred times,' Geordie said warmly.

Jock seemed frightened; the dog was agitated, its tail curled between its legs. It peered round nervously into the darkness behind them. Jock began talking in a foreign language.

'Are you all right, old chap? Can I give you a lift somewhere?'

Pointing at a deep bloody wound on his right hand, Jock was clearly in pain. He shook his head and fell silent.

'Do you need a doctor?'

Jock shrugged his shoulders. He couldn't understand Geordie's question.

'What's your name? I'm Geordie Kinloch.' he pointed at his own chest.

'Stefano.'

'Stefano?' Geordie repeated.

'*Stefano sum.*' He nodded emphatically, pointing at his chest in imitation of Geordie's gesture. He held up his bleeding right hand. '*Sed et facit ut omnes, parvi et magni, divites et pauperes, liberi et servi accipiant characterem in manu sua dextra, aut in frontibus suis.*'

'You what ?' Geordie was quite unprepared for a torrent of Italian at this hour.

'*Et nequis possit emere aut vendere, nisi qui habit characterem aut nomen bestiae, aut numerum nominis eius.*' Stefano spoke agitatedly, looking back frequently over his shoulder towards the cemetery.

'I really don't understand what you're trying to say. Why don't you just hop into the car? We'll find help for you and sort your hand out.' Geordie leaned over to unlock the passenger door. When he turned back to signal to Stefano to get in, the man had gone. Geordie got out of the car. There was no sign of Stefano or his dog in any direction.

'Bloody weird!' He exclaimed as he sat immobile in the car. He reflected for a while then buckled himself back in his seat.

Josie came out of the front door as he drove into the courtyard.

'They're in the house again.'

'Who?'

'Footsteps on the gravel a short while ago, and doors banging.'

Geordie looked alarmed. 'There's weird stuff going on. You know the other evening we were driving back through the glen crossroads, and I saw Jock?'

'Jock? After your London trip? Yes, you were behaving a bit oddly that evening.'

'Well, I see him there quite often. We wave at each other. Just now, as I was driving through the crossroads he came running up to the car. He seemed to be in some distress. His right hand was bleeding quite heavily. I stopped and wound down the window to talk to him. He gabbled away in a foreign language — it sounded like Italian, but it could have been Spanish-- and it didn't make any sense to me.'

'You wave every day to a strange guy in a cemetery and stop for him to come up to the car? Then he speaks Italian? That sounds very dubious you know. You'll get a reputation.'

'Very funny. He was in trouble, his hand was bleeding, so I stopped. He held his right hand in the air and pointed to a wound on it. It seemed like he was warning me.'

'What was he saying?'

'The weird thing is that I recall some of what he said. Though he spoke in Italian, it's as if he was saying it in English.'

'What was he was saying?' She insisted. It was a long shot, but Josie had learned Italian at school and went on an Easter visit to Florence 15 years ago.

He brandished his right hand in my face and I heard him shout words like, *'facit ut omnes, parvi et magni... liberi et servi ...in manu dextra.'* Josie scribbled the words on the back of a notepad. She looked at them for a minute. 'That's Latin, Geordie, not Italian. Literally, I think it means something like, "he made all, small and great, free and slave... on his right hand." What else do you remember him saying?'

'Nothing else. What do you think it signifies?'

'I couldn't tell you, apart from that literal translation. Father Saintey might know what it means. He's the language scholar around here.'

Father Saintey had taught Classics at Fort Augustus for many years. He was a jovial character and always included Balnadarg on his rounds, even though it was a Presbyterian household. The sweet wines of the Kinloch cellar had long since stitched up any sectarian differences that might have separated them. Josie phoned him.

'Geordie says he met an odd chap today who spoke Italian to him.'

'Did he, indeed?'

'He caught scraps of what the man was saying. Actually, it sounds like Latin to me. I wondered if you could make sense of what was being said?'

'By all means. What do you have?'

'Facit ut omnes, parvi et magni ...'

'...divites et pauperes, liberi et servi,' Father Saintey continued the passage as if quoting from a schoolboy poem, *'accipiant characterem in manu sua dextra, aut in frontibus suis.'* He stopped.

'That's easy. Yes that's definitely Latin, not Italian. Chapter 13 of the Book of Revelation. It means, "He forced everyone, small and great, rich and poor, free and slave, to receive a mark on his right hand or his forehead." '

'Why would someone come up to Geordie and say that?'

'Who was this person again?'

'He's an odd fellow I've never met. Geordie calls him Jock, but it turns out he's called Stefano. Geordie often sees him standing by the cemetery at the glen crossroad and waves at him. The odd thing, Father Saintey, is that we were driving together one evening a few weeks ago and Geordie waved at this man, but I didn't see him. Emily said the same thing. Geordie was taking her to a party and he honked at a man by the cemetery. Emily and her friends didn't see anybody. I'm getting a bit worried about Geordie. You don't think he's getting hallucinations, do you? '

'The Kinlochs have always had the gift of The Sight, Josie. You have to respect that.' Father Saintey intoned solemnly, 'Did the man say anything else?'

'He said he was called Stefano, and after saying what I just said to you, Geordie says he continued with something like, *'Et nequis possit emere aut vendere ...'*

'... nisi qui habit characterem aut nomen bestiae aut numerum nominis eius.' Father Saintey completed the verse. 'And that means, as you may know, "And nobody can buy or sell anything unless they possess the mark or the number of the Beast."

'That's spooky.'

'That's Revelation. Have there been any other manifestations around Balnadarg recently?'

'Now you ask, at exactly the time Geordie was speaking to Stefano at the crossroads, I heard footsteps on the gravel and someone entered the house.'

'So it's not just Geordie hearing strange things?'

'I guess not.'

'Look, I think I should come over. Something might be about to happen there.'

'Like what?' Josie was suddenly frightened.

'Can't tell, but I'll be over as quickly as I can. About 40 minutes.'

Geordie was sitting quietly on a sofa in the kitchen sipping a large

whisky while Josie had her conversation with Father Saintey. 'So?'
'He's coming round straight away. He sounded quite serious.
Said he thought something might be about to happen.'
'Like what?'
'He wouldn't say. Except that the Italian you heard was actually
Latin. It was from Chapter 13 of the Book of Revelation.'
Geordie stood and reached for the scruffy pew bible tucked
among Josie's cookery books on the kitchen shelf. He turned to
Chapter 13 of the Book of Revelation.
'Crikey, it's all about the Beast,' Geordie said as he scanned the
verse.
'The Beast?' Josie pretended to sound amused.
'Yes. Here we are: The Beast out of the Sea and the Beast out of
the Earth. All inhabitants of the earth will worship the Beast.'
Father Saintey was deceptively jovial. He was renowned for
winning people over with effortless charm and possessed every good
priest's instinct for what made people tick. He was as relaxed in a
pub quaffing a beer with a janitor as in a Georgian drawing room
sipping tea with a dowager. He was a modest man. He always
underplayed the fact that he was a prodigious biblical scholar, local
historian and Classicist.
Father Saintey listened attentively to Josie's account of footsteps
on the gravel and to Geordie's description of Jock at the crossroads.
'Did you know that Balnadarg was situated on one of the most
powerful ley lines in the world? It runs in a straight line from the
East Coast, all the way to the Island of Iona off the West Coast.
That's a distance of nearly 200 miles.'
'Ley lines?' Josie enquired.
'A ley line is an energy line that crosses the landscape. The
ancients knew about them. They built towns, cathedrals, holy places,
burial grounds and other features along the lines. Many of the finest
cathedrals in France were constructed on ley lines. Parish churches
across the face of England follow ley lines. There are spectacular ley
lines in the Andes. They're to be found all over the world. If you give

me a map of Scotland I will show you how the line runs through Balnadarg.'

Geordie fetched a 19th century Ordnance Survey map of the Southern Highlands and unfolded it on the kitchen table.

'Excellent, an old one. It won't be cluttered with modern features.' Father Saintey studied the map with approval. 'Now follow this line. It starts near Montrose, runs right through the sculptured stones at Aberlemno, straight through Fortingall ...'

'Where the ancient yew tree is?' Josie asked.

'Exactly. Some say it's the oldest tree in Europe. It may be 5000 years old. Whether that is true or not, it was already an old tree when Christ was born. They say Pontius Pilate was born nearby and that Joseph of Arimathea preached in its shade. Of course, that's mythology, but we won't let that get in the way of a good story.'

'Fun to speculate, though.' Geordie commented.

'Indeed. But we need to explore another train of thought right now. You will see how the line goes all the way to Iona, where Saint Columba established a Christian mission in the Hebrides.'

'And there's Balnadarg. Look, the line runs straight through our drawing room.' Josie was exaggerating only a little.

'Indeed. And through the Iron Age mound on your hill, and it coincides with the Roman road ...'

'That goes all the way to the crossroads at the cemetery where Jock hangs out,' Geordie interjected.

'Exactly. This energy line runs directly between Balnadarg and the crossroads.'

'What does that mean?'

'Well, you can go from boring observation to wild fancy, depending on your personal degree of scepticism.' Father Saintey was accustomed to the full range of reactions to his theories.

'I'm merely pointing out that you are situated on an energy line that was identified by the ancients long before Christ, before the Romans, possibly even before the Druids and Celts. Whoever identified these ley lines was attuned to the geomagnetic power of our dear Mother earth and its relationship to the stars and planets. They knew where to situate forts, standing stones, burial mounds and where to build their roads.'

'How does that relate to what's happening here?' Josie asked anxiously.

'I'm suggesting that the footsteps on the nonexistent gravel at Balnadarg and the excited fellow at the crossroads six miles away could be manifestations of a new surge of energy along this ley line. In recent weeks I've also heard about satanic activity in Blackcraig Forest and inexplicable disturbances near Ardchattan Priory. They're both further west along the same ley line.' Father Saintey reflected for a moment, before adding, 'I'm not aware of phenomena like this happening since the 17th century, when there was a surge of witchcraft in the Highlands.'

'Did that coincide with a surge of energy along this actual ley line?' Josie enquired.

'Very possibly. It coincided with a spate of witch hunts and executions in this area. If you go to Forfar, you can see the reconstruction of a medieval witchcraft trial in the local museum. Disturbances in the 17th century were so great in the vicinity of some ley lines that the courts intervened to quash what they thought might be a satanic rebellion against the Crown.'

'Then the energy subsided, the ley lines went quiet and Satanism died down.' Josie was on the edge of her seat.

'That's right. Peace was restored for a few hundred years.'

'So are you suggesting that the ley lines might be re-activating, for want of a better word?' Geordie chipped in.

'Maybe. I don't like the feel of what you've told me. I don't think the Balnadarg manifestation in itself is serious, a simple exorcism could deal with that. But the coincidence of the chap at the crossroads and the Ardchattan disturbances suggest that a current of energy might be building up along the entire length of the ley line.'

'Satanism?' Josie suggested.

'I hesitate to use that word, but possibly. This feels more than just a group of students and superannuated rock stars playing around with satanic symbols. Geordie just saw a chap at the crossroads who had the mark of the beast cut into his hand.'

'Do you think this was the manifestation of an event centuries ago, or a vision of the future?' Geordie asked anxiously.

'That's a very good question. Judging by your overall description, Stefano's name, his clothes and the fact that he used Latin, it would suggest a past event. If he were dressed futuristically or even contemporaneously and spoke Americanized English, I would be extremely worried.' He said this with a twinkle in the eye.

'So what do you think Stefano's story might be?'

'If you look at this map, you will note that your crossroads is at the junction of a Roman road. The cemetery is situated beside a field called Gallowfauld. I wouldn't be surprised if a set of gallows had been set up at the crossroads by the Romans. It's on high ground and it's visible from a distance. The Romans liked to execute criminals at places like this, by hanging, decapitation or crucifixion, and to leave the corpses for the birds and wolves to devour. Mangled corpses were a salutary warning to criminals and Caledonian dissidents.'

'So you think that Stefano might have been executed there?'

'Very possibly.'

'But what was the bloody mark on his hand?'

'Ordinarily, people might say it was a crucifixion mark, but I don't think so. Despite countless depictions of Christ having nails driven through the palm of his hands, Roman executioners were more likely to drive the nail through the victim's wrist. The palm of your hand is soft and fleshy and the body's weight would tear the nail through your hand very quickly. A nail through your wrist would hold the body's weight more effectively.'

'So how might he have died?'

'Did you notice any marks on his skin? Red marks around his neck, arrow marks, contusions on his body that might indicate he had been stoned?'

'Can't say that I did.'

'A pity,' Father Saintey said absent-mindedly, 'It might have been St Stephen.' He sat down and put his hands behind his head, staring at the ceiling.

'Could Stefano be an ancient Christian martyr delegated to send a warning to us?' Geordie speculated, 'Perhaps somehow he only managed to get his message across by being carved with the Mark of the Beast ?'

'That means, of course, that he would have lost God's protection once he allowed himself to be marked. A double bluff is unlikely. Revelation says quite clearly that if anyone receives the mark of the beast on the forehead or on the hand, "he too will drink of the wine of God's fury". That makes me think that your friend Stefano is more likely to be one of Satan's men.'

By this time Josie was thoroughly alarmed. 'So you're saying that Balnadarg is on a kind of spiritual battle line. How can we protect ourselves?'

'You need to be aware and sensible. I will perform an exorcism around the castle this evening, as a precaution. I will also do the same on your Iron Age mound and around your yew trees. I'll go to the crossroads and try to lay Stefano to rest. That should hold the fort until we get a fuller picture of what's going on. I'm aware of serious concerns in the Vatican about current happenings. I'll need to confer with my colleagues to see how they're dealing with similar phenomena cropping up in other parts of the world.'

Father Saintey looked like an Old Testament prophet as he incanted his spiritual message around the walls of Balnadarg. The exorcism did not produce any side effects. There were no banshees or bangs.

'Your visitor knew he didn't belong here. He muttered a few oaths at me, picked up his hat and coat, and departed. He won't be back for a while.' Father Saintey announced after a few minutes. Josie smiled in relief at Geordie, who shrugged his shoulders in response.

Geordie accompanied the old priest to the Iron Age mound across the fields. He began to walk around the base of the mound, repeating again and again, 'In Jesus name I bid all evil spirits to be banished from this place, in Jesus' name…' After walking two thirds of the way around the mound Father Saintey leaned forward like a wrestler. His arms seemed to be pushing against an invisible object, like a rugby player in a scrum. He puffed and sweated,

'In … Jesus'… name…I … bid …all … evil … spirits … to … be …banished … from … this … place … in … Jesus' … name …'

A blast of wind twisted and bent the yew trees high up on the mound. Small branches and twigs spiralled in a vortex high above them. A herd of belted Galloway cattle had been munching grass peaceably in the adjacent field. With an unearthly bellow they bucked and kicked like rodeo steers. They raced across the field in an angry mob. Geordie thought they would crash through the five bar gate and flatten him to a pulp with Father Saintey, but 20 yards short of a collision, the cattle skidded to a halt, calmed down and began grazing again, as if nothing had happened.

Father Saintey steadied himself on Geordie's arm. 'Remember when Christ exorcised the demons that flew across and possessed the herd of swine?'

Geordie nodded. 'The Gadarene swine?'

'I think we've just witnessed something similar.'

Life returned to normal at Balnadarg after these events. The Kinloch family got on with their daily rounds.

Three months later, Geordie was wakened by the light of a full moon playing across his face in the bedroom. It was 2 o'clock. The night was warm and as calm as a pool of water. He rose out of bed and stood by the window to look at the play of silver moonlight in the trees and fields. The folds of the fields were clearly visible, as were the still, dark lumps that represented his beloved cattle. Nearer to the house, his eyes narrowed towards a dark patch on the lawn. He looked hard and made out a figure standing there. The person stood still and patiently. A dog lay at his feet. They both faced the house.

Geordie froze. Without conveying his fear to Josie, he shook her gently.

'I thought you should see outside. It's such a beautiful moon tonight. I hope you don't mind me waking you up.'

She looked at the bedside clock, yawned and wasn't happy to be disturbed, 'Dammit Geordie, it's 2 o'clock. We've got a busy day tomorrow.'

'I know. But you're awake now. Come and look at the beautiful moon.'

She shuffled out of bed, pulled a dressing gown over her shoulders and looked out of the open window. Geordie stood behind her. 'Now isn't that a beautiful sight?' The moon bathed the trees with silver. He wanted to draw her attention to the figure on the lawn, but without actually pointing it out.

'Look at the light reflecting off the pond.' Geordie cooed, 'It's so romantic, isn't it?' The pond was directly behind the figure. There was no way she could have admired the pond without observing the figure. Yet she replied, 'It's fabulous, Honey. I've never seen anything so romantic.'

The scene was like a Chinese painting, with willows trailing their branches into the moonlit pond, its surface shimmering with circles from the waterfall. From behind Josie's back, Geordie waved his hand at the figure on the lawn. His blood chilled when it waved back. He imagined the Mark of the Beast in the darkness.

It was clear that the figure was not visible to Josie. She tugged his hand, 'Come on Darling, come back to bed.' They lay down. Dozily, she whispered, 'I'm so happy you woke me to see the full moon.'

It was a light breezy morning. Small white clouds scudded across the summer sky; cattle grazed in the park with their calves. It could not have been a more idyllic, peaceful sight. Geordie picked up the phone: 'Father Saintey? Sorry to disturb you, but I wanted to share something with you.'

He described the apparition on the lawn, acknowledging that he might have imagined the whole thing. Father Saintey paused to digest what Geordie was saying, then spoke in his confidential, quiet way, 'Unfortunately, Geordie, you didn't imagine it. There have been increasing troubles all along this ley line, and others throughout the world. The devil's on the loose, my friend. He's watching us. I don't think we have much time. We need to talk urgently.'

'Why don't you come round this afternoon on a social pretext? I don't want to alarm the family but I'd like to talk to you about what's happening.'

'3 o'clock?'

'3 o'clock. And don't forget to bring your exorcist's kit!' Geordie's attempt at levity fell on deaf ears. Father Saintey replied, 'A very small finger in a very large dyke, I'm afraid.'

Geordie filled a cafetiere and retreated to the conservatory with a newspaper. On the correspondence page of the paper, a group of well-known global politicians had written an open letter to amend the Permanent Universal Identity Directive from Brussels. The letter began by describing why the Act was being brought into law. It was so that every person might have one single, permanent, totally convenient source of identification. It was proposed that all official cards, such as passports, driving licences and social security cards should be combined into one document. It would contain finger prints, DNA and retinal data, and would be utterly impossible to forge.

It was further proposed that every citizen of Europe should have such a card. Discussions were under way to coordinate cards with the Chinese, Indians, the Afro Asia Free Trade Zone and the NAFTA Bloc. In other words, it was anticipated that every government in the world would support the proposal.

Geordie sipped thoughtfully from his coffee cup, stared over the top of the paper for a moment, and read on. 'The technology now exists for all information to be stored on a single multi-gig, self-charging, expandable Total Identity Chip (TIC) the size of a grain of rice. We recommend that every citizen of the world should receive an implant immediately after the Act becomes law. After considerable research our consultants have concluded that, in order to respect freedom of choice for all citizens, individuals might choose to have their chip implanted in the back of their right hand or in their forehead.'

The article covered the whole page, extolling the fantastic convenience of TICs. Mankind would be elevated to a state of Information Nirvana. Universal Sensors would be available in banks, airports, schools, hospitals, supermarkets, office buildings and on the streets. In short, they would be everywhere, so that everyone would be interconnected with a gargantuan database at all times. TICs would be invisible to the naked eye, "so there would be no cosmetic detriment."

The article concluded "We are proud to announce that we have almost attained unanimity on this proposal. We have the signatures of 643 presidents. A further 23 could not be reached at the time of going to press, but have signalled their agreement with the proposal and will sign in the next month."

When Father Saintey entered the house, Geordie shook his hand cordially and gave him the printed letter he'd read earlier that morning. 'I think Revelation is about to be fulfilled. What do you think?'

'Without doubt. The question, my friend, is which side of the fence you choose to be on.'

The Bunny Patrol

Geordie began to get involved in various charitable activities. He wanted to donate time and as much of the quirky Kinloch life experience as the world might find useful. He enjoyed contributing, but it felt somewhat out of character to be considered altruistic for the first time in his life. In his soul he wasn't really the bleeding heart type. What surprised him was that most people he dealt with in this new world were not either.

'If they find a mobile phone in your cell you can kiss goodbye to parole and all your good conduct credits,' the prisoner informed Geordie. He was a rotund, affable-looking chap. Like many criminals he was to meet, he was well-spoken, articulate and plausible; not at all the sort of man you'd have expected to be put away for fraud and embezzlement. Geordie had also made friends with murderers, who, on the face of it, he would have trusted to drink tea with his granny.

'But you can't run a business without a mobile these days,' he continued, 'How else can you stay in touch with your customers from inside? You have to keep in their face or there'll be no customers left when you get out.'

'I suppose that makes good business sense.' Geordie agreed absent-mindedly, not quite realizing that he could be accused of abetting a prisoner.

'Prison officers rip your cell apart as soon as they suspect you have a mobile. But you've got to be incredibly stupid to let that happen. Snooping officers always give themselves away when they pad around. The prisoners will whistle, jeer and rattle their cages if they suspect they're being snooped on. There's plenty time to hide the mobile and take up your knitting by the time they kick open your cell door. It's amazing how prisoners manage to hide things from POs after all this time.'

'So how do you hide it?' Geordie was fascinated by the prison subculture.

'I'll come to that.' the prisoner replied, holding up his left hand to counsel patience.

'Just interested.'

'Look, it's a matter of playing the game. If you're stupid enough to be caught with a mobile in your hand when they bust your cell, you deserve what's coming. The prison officer's got no choice but to crack you. They wear helmet-mounted cameras and your crime is on line as soon as they see you. You give them no choice.'

'Doesn't that infringe your human rights?'

'Only if they secretly film you without you knowing. Look, the POs have to prove to the governor that they're in charge, so they make their quota of busts every week. You just have to be sure you're not one of them.' Geordie was struck by the Tom & Jerry affection and antipathy between the players at the jail.

'So how do you hide the phone?' Geordie persisted.

The prisoner looked around warily.

'You've already taken off the case before the mobile comes into the prison, right? You strip it down to a mess of circuits and slip it into your radio. If they look inside the radio—which they don't, particularly if it's on when the PO's burst in—all they see is the electronics. If you've been clever, your mobile has been slotted in like a glove.'

'What do you do with the plastic case?'

'It comes off before it gets into the prison.'

'So you're dealing with just the skeleton of a mobile?'

'You could say that but you've got to be mindful not to slip a Nokia circuit board into a Sony radio. The wrong board sticks out like a pork chop in a synagogue.'

'Doesn't all this process take time?' Geordie pressed him.

'When I make a call, I leave open the back of my radio. I can stop the call, replace the mobile, close the radio and take up my book in six seconds. That's faster than any PO can catch me.' He reflected for a moment, adding, 'So far'.

'But if the POs need to make a quota of successful busts each week, how do they do it? You'd think they would have got wise to the prisoners by now.'

'They're wise all right. They know what's going on. But there are plenty of new prisoners who don't know the game. They're the ones who get nabbed- in the early years. I've never known a long-termer who got nabbed after they've been here two years or more. I've been here eight years. It's been seven since I was caught. But they're tightening up. They have to make new busts. That's why we have the Bunny Patrol.'

'The Bunny Patrol?'

'Aye, the Bunny Patrol. Prison officers are in the habit of creeping around the cell block from outside. They creep under the ledge of your window and listen for any phone conversations. If they can trace a phone transmission back to your cell, they give a radio signal and the other POs break in.'

'Caught red-handed.'

'Aye, red-handed. That's why we have the Bunny Patrol. Some of the lads breed rabbits as part of animal care for their rehabilitation programme. It's funny to watch a mass murdering drug dealing thug handle a bunny with such tenderness. They sneak them out in their pocket and free them on the lawn. The grass is good and the bunnies don't usually leave—unless a buzzard gets them.'

This innocent ruse reminded Geordie of the devious tricks employed by wartime British prisoners of war. The amount of undetected tunnelling that went on under German prison camps was amazing. Hiding a mobile phone in today's world was child's play by comparison.

'So whenever a PO creeps about outside, the bunnies scatter. When the bunnies graze peacefully, there are no Prison Officers. If the bunnies run away, something's frightened them.'

'So you don't need to be on the lookout for stealthy prison officers all the time.'

'Naa. We just have to be on the lookout for bunnies in the middle of the lawn. We have a kid watching the bunnies from a corner cell window. When the bunnies scatter, he gives a signal.'

'What kind of signal ?'

'A very loud sneeze. You'd be amazed how the sound carries through the Wing.'

'So that's the Bunny Patrol?'

'That's the Bunny Patrol. A traditional solution to a modern problem.'

'Don't the prison officers have any idea of this?'

'You know,' the prisoner said reflectively, 'Sometimes I think they know, but they let it carry on. They could easily shoot all the bunnies on the grass. It would take ten minutes with a .22 . But every prison needs a safety valve or it would explode. The Bunny Patrol is our safety valve here'.

Geordie handed back his keys and signed out. As he left the prison complex he turned up his coat collar, leaned into the bitter wind, turned into the street and joined the flow of the crowd. He felt uneasy as he mulled over his conversation with the prisoner.

Reflecting on some of his professional friends, indeed, his own behaviour on occasion, he came to a gloomy conclusion. The only difference between a criminal and the average apparently innocent man was that one had been caught and the other hadn't --yet.

Le Canigou

He greatly looked forward to attending his first alumni reunion at the OU Club. In the 20 years since he'd graduated he'd never attended a reunion. He'd kept up with a handful of friends but had lost track of most. This was possibly his last opportunity to catch up with everyone in his year—another 20 years, and the ranks would be thinning.

As he entered the club a matronly woman bounded up from across the lobby. 'Geordie! What a surprise to see you here!'

'How lovely to see you again!' he replied enthusiastically, racking his memory. 'You haven't changed a bit. Goodness, how long has it been? Fifteen, twenty years?'

The woman's effusiveness turned to dust. 'What *are* you talking about? We sat together at the opera last week. Aida, Covent Garden, dinner at Jack's, Celia's 50th...?'

Geordie had just made a complete arse of himself.

'Oh blimey, I'm so terribly sorry. I'm here for a university alumni dinner. I assumed ...'

She muttered 'Bloody fool', and turned tail, disappearing into the Ladies' cloakroom.

He caught the doorman's amused eye: 'Dammit! That wasn't the first time and won't be the last.' Geordie shook his head in embarrassment.

After consulting the doorman he made his way through the crowded bar and climbed upstairs to a function room. On the left was an open space where knots of people were gathered, chattering amiably. To the right, numerous tables were set for dinner. He picked a glass of champagne off a passing tray and plunged in.

The air was thick with that old lie: "Good Lord, you haven't changed a bit!" but life had been kinder to some than others. It was striking how many of the quiet ones at university had blossomed. Several men radiated successful careers and held court confidently at the centre of attentive groups. Geordie recalled the "Wee Mary" syndrome. These were girls who studied all the time and were never seen at the Union bar. Two glamorous 40-something ladies stood laughing in the midst of a veritable honeypot of men. Their long hours in the library had clearly paid dividends.

On the other hand, many former players in the old fast crowd had fared less well. Some had gained weight, others were balding and wrinkled, many looked battered by serial career and conjugal misadventures. One man who looked like he'd been treated to courses of Botox sidled up to Geordie,

'I thought you were dead.' was his first overture for 20 years. It caused much amusement in the surrounding group.

'Did you miss me?' Geordie laughed. He was tempted to add, 'And how's Annika?' The tabloids had recently revealed a steamy incident between his soon-to-be ex-wife and a young jockey. But he held his tongue; actually he felt quite benevolent towards his old friend.

'Not at all, ha ha.' The fellow then banged on about how he'd made millions on oil deals in Africa, and how well-connected he was, and how many grouse he'd shot at his brother's estate in Scotland last season, and, and …

There was Nathan! He sported thick grey locks which used to be thick black locks. A bored blonde floozy was on his arm. He apologized that he couldn't stay for dinner because of a long-standing prior engagement. Little had changed: different hair, different bored floozy, same excuses. Geordie patted Nathan's shoulder in a gesture of bonhomie. They exchanged cards while wallowing in exuberant promises to keep in touch. Both knew they never would.

And there was Diana, a love from his college days. She had aged well, but not so well as to inspire regret. How she'd run him ragged back then! On off on off maybe on, maybe off maybe NO… Her greying husband drank heavily and stood aloof with a gimlet eye on the proceedings. Geordie felt an inexplicable surge of affinity for him and hoped it had all been worthwhile.

After dinner there was a general swap of guests around the tables. People shuffled here and there and sat with different groups. Geordie homed in on Ed Bramwell, holding court confidently at the head of his table. Twenty years earlier they'd shared a rowdy flat with six others. They hadn't been particularly close at the time, but Geordie had always liked him for his humour, intelligence and self-deprecating honesty.

'Hey, Ed!' Geordie peered theatrically under the table. 'Just checking your shoes. You always wore army boots at university.'

'You haven't changed at all.' Seeing Geordie's sceptical look, he added, 'No, really.' Ed's ensuing belly laugh hadn't changed either. He rose from his chair and the old mates hugged.

'I want to hear everything you've been up to since we last met.'

Ed introduced Geordie to his wife Moira, a dark-eyed Scottish artist.

'After uni, we went to France and set up a textile business in the Ardeche. That didn't work too well, so I got into marketing.'

'What kind of marketing?'

'All sorts of marketing over the years, but for the past five years I've been helping charities to raise funds and market themselves.'

What charities in particular?' Geordie enquired.

'One is a charity in memory of a friend's son. He was training to be a teacher and drowned in a freak boating accident at the age of 21. The only way his parents could make any sense of their loss was to set up a charity in his memory. He had adored children. His parents realized pretty quickly that any money raised would go much further overseas than in the UK. He'd once done a summer stint in Romania as a student, helping kids. So all the money we raise for his charity goes to helping AIDS children at an orphanage outside Bucharest. This is exactly what he would have liked.'

'What a fantastic way of handling an unbearable situation.'

'Well, they simply had to do something to respond to what had happened. Actually, I'm organizing a sponsored hike in the Pyrenees from August to October this year. We'll hike along the

Haute Route, starting on the Atlantic Coast on August 26th and I hope to finish on the Mediterranean in the second week of October. My route covers the best part of a thousand kilometres. I'll be joined by sponsored walkers all along the way.'

'Do you still have room for walkers?'

'Sure, but the sooner you book your slot the better your chances of getting the week you want. Some weeks are fuller than others.'

'Well, let me know because I'd love to join you for a stretch.'

'I'll email you with details and available dates. You can let me know.'

They reminisced about mutual friends, their crazy life experiences, their hopes and fears. Ed had lived a full life yet always kept his quiver full of plans. Geordie admired that. As fast as Ed fulfilled an ambition, another sprang up to replace it. Ed enjoyed every minute of every day and always looked forward.

Geordie spoke to a few more friends before heading into the damp Soho night. He was content to have caught up with the handful he'd spoken to and mildly disappointed about the dozens he had not. But he promised himself not to leave it another 20 years.

The Easyjet flight touched down in Toulouse. As it taxied to the gate the plane halted to let an Airbus Beluga take off. The colossal aircraft thundered down the runway and soared with surprising grace into the western sky. It was an omen for Geordie. Such an unlikely contraption in the air somehow reassured him that even he would be able to hike the high Pyrenees.

He was met outside the baggage area by Bill Justice, a friend of Ed Bramwell's. Bill's role was to support the hikers by meeting them each evening at pre-appointed refuges in the mountains along the route. He transported their kit from refuge to refuge, delivering plentiful supplies of food, chilled beer and sticking plaster after every day's slog. Each morning the hikers would load their packs into Bill's car and set out, carrying only what they needed for a day in the mountains. Bill then had 8 hours to drive to the next refuge, where he met the weary hikers with their kit again.

Geordie liked Bill immediately. He was in his early 60s with long grey hair, a beard, smiling blue eyes and an open, Scottish face. He laughed a lot.

'So where are we heading to now?' Geordie asked as he loaded his pack into the rear of a battered Citroën.

'L'Hospitalet-près- l'Andorre. It's about two hours. We meet Ed at the Hotel Dupuy in the middle of the village. We'll have dinner on arrival, followed by a good kip and breakfast at 7 in the morning. After breakfast you'll load your kit into Sylvie—he patted the car's roof—and off you go into the wild blue yonder.'

'Who's Ed hiking with right now?'

'He was with two friends who stopped hiking in Andorra yesterday. I'm taking them back to the airport at the weekend and picking up another couple who'll start hiking next week.'

'So I'm alone with Ed for a few days?'

'Yes, that's right.'

'I hope I'm in good enough condition. He's been hiking in these mountains for weeks and must be incredibly fit by now.'

'He is, but he's used to pale townies arriving from the UK to hike with him every week. You'll be OK, I promise you.'

Bill left the airport behind and headed south west towards the distant Pyrenees.

'Has anybody had a problem with altitude on this expedition?'

'The highest mountains you will climb are in the 2,500 to 2,900-metre range. My understanding, unless you're a seriously sea-level kind of guy, is that altitude sickness doesn't really kick in until you're well over 3,000 metres. But there's always a first time.'

'Hope you're right.' Geordie muttered as he viewed the jagged peaks of the mountain range silhouetted sharply against the late afternoon sky.

The scenery darkened and the road twisted as they gained height. They drove through many mountain villages clustered at the bottom of deep canyons.

'Who on earth lives in these places?'

'An unholy mix of montagnards: shepherds, foresters, tour guides, hydro- electric maintenance guys, artists, poets, British nutters, the occasional Parisienne with a history...'

'They come here to forget, like in the Foreign Legion?'

'Or to be forgotten,' Bill laughed. 'They recently found a couple of Belgians up here who'd been involved in a bank fraud back in the 80s.'

'It's amazing how the sun sets so much earlier at the bottom of the valley. If you look at the peaks there's still sunlight up there.' Geordie craned to see the top of a mountain on the left, the autumnal aspens glowing gold on its flank. He began to feel queasy and tried to doze off.

'Welcome to L'Hospitalet-près- l'Andorre.' Geordie jolted from his half-sleep as Bill pulled into the car park of the Hotel Dupuy. It was a sturdy square stone building. Its red lights gave it a festive feel, though Geordie had other urgent things to consider. Another 10 minutes of uphill, twisty, sick-inducing driving, and he would have gone over the top. Bill knew the signs, watched carefully and had timed it perfectly.

The moment the car stopped, Geordie jerked the handle, threw open the door and staggered towards a stone parapet. He puked resoundingly into a fast flowing mill-race that fed into the local hydro-electric plant.

'That'll be good for half a kilowatt.' Bill observed drily 'You all right?'

'Oh, peachy.'

'Take your time old chap. I'll get your stuff out of the car.'

Geordie opened his arms and stretched, taking in huge gulps of oxygen. The chilled mountain air, the spray of rushing water and his unburdened stomach improved his condition immediately. He began to feel hungry.

Ed's full-bellied laughter could be heard in the bar from the car park. They found him holding court before a group of bemused

Catalan construction workers, explaining why Britain was so aloof from Europe. He wore pyjamas at the bar which nobody seemed to think odd: this was just another perfectly normal aloof Englishman. After a couple of chilled beers and bowls of pot au feu by the bar, the travellers hit the hay.

L'Hospitalet was at 1,500 metres and the first day's hike would take them to the Coll de Coma d'Anyell at 2,470 metres. They would then descend to the next refuge at Bouillouses, a horizontal distance of about 18 kilometres. After an unsatisfying breakfast of bread, jam and *café au lait* Geordie got booted and spurred, loaded his kit into Sylvie and prepared for the starting gun.

Ed tightened the straps on his day pack, patted himself down to check for his compass, wallet, maps, sunglasses, sandwiches and water bottle. He tapped his stick on the ground. 'Right! Let's go.' With a baleful look, Geordie turned back and waved at Bill, who grinned back: *'A bientôt.'*

They passed geranium-festooned water troughs and stone cattle sheds as they began hiking through the village. Nobody was around. At the far end they climbed a crude stair hacked into the rock, which led to a woodland track. For three hours they plodded steadily upwards through a long valley consisting of pine trees and alpine meadows. They encountered grazing cows with bells, amiable wild horses and thousands of butterflies rising off carpets of autumn crocuses. The aspens turning gold and the scent of myriads of pines in the dry autumn sunshine were intoxicating.

'Pretty spectacular, eh?' Ed had set a steady pace which Geordie was handling comfortably.

To their left they passed a glacial lake. The path began to climb steeply towards a chalet high above them.

'That's the Refuge des Bésines. We'll stop there for a break.'

By the time they reached the chalet Geordie felt dizzy and disoriented. His vision was blurred as if by bright lights and he couldn't talk clearly.

'You all right, old chap?' he heard Ed's voice as if it were coming from a dream.

'Well, yes, I think so. Mmm....yes, I think so.' His own voice sounded distant. 'I'm going to lie down for a few minutes.' He collapsed onto a bed of heather and shut his eyes. His head was swimming; blood swished loudly through his brain.

'Here, take this.' Ed passed him a water bottle 'Take a good swig: it's got vitamin C in it. You might just be dehydrated.'

They stopped for 15 minutes, during which they gulped water, chewed high energy bars and relieved themselves behind a huge boulder. Geordie felt much better.

'Right! Time marches on,' Ed announced, shouldering his day pack. 'Let's *frapper la route.*'

'You what?'

'Hit the road.' He peered at the map. 'We're coming up to the Colle de Coma d'Anyell at 2,470 metres. Just take it slowly. We don't want to find out why it's called Daniel's Coma, do we?'

Geordie was beginning to understand Ed's tortuous and witty use of language, weaving English, French and Spanish into a pun-filled argot comprehensible only to the undergraduate multi-linguist.

Five hours later, long after they'd come off the Colle and swum in the frigid waters of a small lake, they plodded up to the Refuge des Bouillouses, a square stone house similar to the one in which they'd stayed the previous night.

Bill was waiting like a cat by the fireside. He sat reading a book in the evening sun, beers at the ready.

'I've put your kit on your bunks, upstairs to the left.' Bill jerked his thumb in the general direction. 'We've been allocated the first three on the left. It's a full house tonight so you should take your showers and use the facilities sooner rather than later.'

The arrangement in these mountain refuges was communal sleeping, communal eating and communal ablutions for about 30 Euros a night. It provided a perfect opportunity for testing European solidarity, Geordie reflected, as he lay in his upper bunk that night. Two Italians, two Germans, a Belgian, three Catalans and three Brits slept in the dormitory. Dinner had been a passable beef stew, a sumptuous chocolate mousse and copious vin de table. Geordie drifted off to a cosmopolitan cacophony of snoring, grunting, wheezing and farting, relieved that he'd survived the day without holding back Ed's relentless schedule for hiking the Pyrenees.

Each day started in a similar way. There would be a rush to the porcelain hole that passed for a toilet, a rush to the *douche* that ran cold after three short showers, a rush to the refectory to grab two bits of bread and a *café au lait,* then often as not, a rush back to the porcelain hole. To avoid incidents this routine had to be executed tactfully, in a way that one foreigner did not seem to be elbowing other foreigners aside.

After breakfast Ed and Geordie heaved their kit into Sylvie for transporting to the next location. Yet again, they tied their laces, filled water bottles, packed sandwiches, shouldered their packs, tightened straps, waved farewell to Bill and began their day's journey.

Day Four was no different as the lads set out in the morning mist from the refuge de Mariailles . The first four kilometres consisted of a steady climb alongside a rushing stream through fragrant forests of pine and birch. They were ascending quite steeply but the tree cover and mist kept them cool. Geordie had learned the importance of an early start: try not to attempt the steepest ascents in the heat of the day. Gradually the forest cover petered out and the morning mist burned off in the sunshine. Their path opened into a vast rocky bowl. Straight ahead, four kilometres in front of them, the walls of the bowl loomed. They were steep, but did not look insurmountable,

'Just a long slog and we'll be on the summit of Canigou by lunchtime,' Ed reckoned, 'and I've got a special treat when we get there.'

They trudged across the treeless, waterless, rocky, dusty wilderness, ascending steadily and stopping frequently. On one break Geordie wiped the sweat from his face and took a long swig from his bottle.

'You know, we should be proud of ourselves. Not many folks

have what it takes to do what we're doing.'

'Don't be so sure.' Ed pointed at a line of people far below snaking up the valley trail behind them.

'There must be 20 people in that crowd.'

'Yeah, out for their Sunday constitutional. Come on, we mustn't let them catch us up. We're supposed to be the fit ones.'

Yet catch up they did; one by one, the members of the Perpignan Diving Club yomped wordlessly past them. They were led by two athletic guys who looked like sports coaches, followed by three Asian women, a string of teenagers, a small fluffy dog, a couple of fattish women and six Catalan men of various ages.

'Sorry to say, Geordie, but an awful lot of folks have what it takes to climb here—In fact, looking at that crowd, I'd say that practically everyone has what it takes.'

'Yeah, not to mention the small dog.'

As they reached the base of the bowl, the path divided. One path zigzagged across the face of the bowl until it reached the ridge that led to the summit; the other headed west to the base of a 100 metre vertical cliff. A split signpost pointed in two directions; each indicated Le Canigou.

'It's pretty obvious which way to go.' said Geordie. 'We'll go straight here, get up on the ridge and reach the summit on the path along the ridge.'

At that moment, a party of three middle-aged women reached the signpost. Without hesitation they turned westwards on the path leading to the vertical cliff. One of them wore what looked like carpet slippers.

'There's your answer,' said Ed 'You can't claim to have had the full Canigou experience unless you take that route'.

Geordie stared at the cliff with horror.

'There is absolutely no way I can go that way. I'm not fit enough, we don't have the kit. Besides, I don't have a head for heights. I'd fall off.'

'That's no problem, Geordie. You take the easier route and we'll meet at the top. I'll race you.'

Geordie turned uphill and began the zigzag route. He was the only person on it. Everyone else—teenagers, oriental women, Catalans, the lady wearing slippers, the small fluffy dog, had unhesitatingly elected the cliff face route.

It occurred to Geordie that the main reason he'd come on this adventure was to accompany Ed. He was surely in dereliction of duty by splitting and taking a different route. Ed had said nothing; he didn't need to comment. Geordie was in a funk. But what if something happened to him on the rock face? What would their friends and his family think when they found out that Geordie had chickened out and abandoned Ed in his hour of need?

Or worse, what if Geordie tripped and broke an ankle on the easy route? He would never live it down.

He swore and retraced his steps.

'If they can do it, I can certainly do it.' Recalling a school motto from long ago, he muttered *'Plus est en vous ...'*

He yomped along the western path until he caught up with Ed, who beamed when he saw Geordie coming up from behind .

'So glad you decided to come this way. I don't know if you'd ever have felt the same satisfaction if you'd taken the easy route to the summit of Canigou. By the way, look!'

Ed pointed at a tiny white dot tracing across the cliff face. 'That's the little dog which passed us an hour ago. Come on, we can do it.'

It was one o'clock; the sun was beating into the bowl, the black rock shimmered. They joined the queue. Yes, there was a queue of people eager to ascend the suicide route. Looking up, Geordie saw spots of pastel and luminescent orange spaced ten metres apart all up the cliff face. The highest was about 90 metres up, the lowest had just started. The Perpignan Diving Club was on its way.

'What amazes me is the total absence of fear in this crowd. They're queuing as if for a fairground ride, laughing and chattering in anticipation of their turn.' Geordie marvelled.

'First of all you probably have up to 200 people a day going this way. There's safety in numbers. It's a well-worn track, the rescue teams are never far away. Secondly, Le Canigou is an iconic mountain to the Catalan. Some of these folks have waited years to do this pilgrimage. They'd never let fear show even if they felt it.'

Ed nodded towards three women who'd laid out a picnic on a red and white chequered tablecloth at the base of the cliff. They were very jolly as they passed round a bottle of red wine, munching on baguettes and admiring the lower anatomy of one of the Perpignan guides.

'OK mate, it's us now. Don't look up, don't look down. Look for holds on the rock face. Treat the whole exercise step by step. Before you know you'll be at the top. Follow me.'

Ed grabbed a protruding rock made shiny by generations of Catalan hands. He pulled himself onto a ledge. He traversed along the ledge until he found another rock, heaved himself onto another ledge, traversed along the ledge ...

Ed was on his third traverse when he yelled, 'Come on Geordie. You're holding up the queue. It's easy.'

Geordie grabbed the shiny rock, pulled himself onto the ledge and started traversing. His legs shook; he was numb. The guy below him shouted encouragement in Catalanglais: *'Vas-y monsieur.* Chill out. I'm a montagnard. I help you.'

'N..no, that's fine.' It wasn't long before Geordie's tentative steps found their place and he began to make steady progress up the cliff. There was a zen to it: by keeping a fair distance between Ed and the Catalan it was like being on a ski tow. An invisible groove had been worn across the face of the cliff: keep in your groove and everyone gets to the top.

The rock wall narrowed into a steep gulley. Climbers were bunched at the bottom, crowding out the safe ledges and grips. Geordie paused. For the first time he looked below. 'Bloody hell. If I slip, it's a straight drop of 150 feet before I hit the rocks. My body will then bounce and fall another 600 feet before coming to rest in a mangled heap way down below.'

'Don't think about it, mate.' Ed shouted encouragingly. 'Enjoy the break. It'll only be a few minutes before the gulley clears and we can move ahead.' A dislodged rock about the size of an orange came clattering down, bounced off the ledge between Geordie and the Catalan and ricocheted through space before hitting a boulder and shattering far below. The Catalan lost his cool.

'Merde alors. Qu'est ce qu'ils font la haut?'

The man swung off his ledge, overtook Geordie and Ed and reached the jammed knot of climbers in a few deft moves. After a brief discussion during which it appeared that one of them had lost his nerve, the Catalan swung out again and climbed the gulley with the agility of Spiderman. When he reached the top he vanished. Moments later he reappeared with a rope, secured it to a vertical rock chimney and threw it over the edge, where it dangled beside the stuck climbers.

One by one they heaved themselves up and vanished over the top, followed by Ed and Geordie. The summit consisted of a sharp rocky platform a few metres square. Every available space was occupied by picnicking families, kids, dogs, pensioners, young and old. A tall iron cross marked the summit. It was festooned with coloured strips of cloth fluttering in the wind, Tibet-style.

If the hard route had seemed crowded, the easy route was delivering dozens of people to the summit. Ed took off his pack, extracted a label-less bottle, unwired it and passed it to Geordie:

'Here—congratulations on making it to the top of Le Canigou, 2,784 metres.'

Geordie peered over the edge of the gulley. 'I cannot believe we just climbed up that thing.' He toasted Ed and swigged a mouthful of fizzy wine.

'Very nice, thanks.' He handed the bottle back to Ed. 'You know, I was completely, utterly, shit-scared down there.'

'Yeah, but don't you feel good now you've done it? Nobody can ever take that away from you. If you really want to know, I was scared too. I'll wager that 90 per cent of the people who come that way are terrified. They just don't admit it.'

Ed and Geordie found a spot and unwrapped their baguettes of cheese and ham.

Three birds with enormous wingspans soared lazily on the thermal currents far above, occasionally swooping closer to the summit in the hope of scraps.

'See those?' Ed pointed to the sky.

'Yeah. They look ready to pick off the odd unwary climber.'

'Vulturius Prandius Vulgaris,' Ed casually tossed out a scientific-sounding name.

'It's pretty impressive that you know their Latin name'.

'Otherwise known as Common Luncheon Vultures'. Ed said casually with a sparkling eye.

They descended on an easy path which zigzagged down the back of le Canigou. The friends chattered amicably, passing a steady flow of hikers heading up and down.

'Will you be going to next year's reunion at the OU Club in London?' Ed asked.

'Sure—Who knows? Next time I might end up doing Everest for charity.'

They reached the Refuge des Cortalets about 4pm, where Bill sat reading a newspaper in the sunshine at a table on the terrasse.

'Ah yes, thought you'd be here any minute.' He looked over his spectacles and slid two chilled artisanal beers across the table. 'How was your day?'

Ashes to ashes

It was a lovely July morning. The parkland trees radiated with wellbeing; their rounded canopies stretched into the sky in enjoyment of the first real warmth of the Highlands that summer. Geordie chucked the heavy polythene bag casually into the back of the old Jaguar as his younger brother Archie buckled himself into the front passenger seat. As he turned the ignition key, he looked across to Archie.

'You OK?'

'Yep, let's go.'

Before long they were barrelling up the A9 in light traffic. A few miles north of Dunkeld they passed Kinnaird House, an imposing square mansion set back a mile from the road and framed by its estate of hills and forests.

'That's where Dad was billeted in 1942 with the 26/92 Battery of the 17th Field Regiment of the Royal Artillery.' Archie had always prided himself on the accuracy of his family knowledge.

'I think I knew that.' Geordie replied.

'I've always loved the story when he had his accident and was laid out on a stretcher by the fireplace in the hall. His batman kneeled down to him. Dad was touched, thinking he was going to hear kind words of support through his pain, and that he might have the chance to dictate a short letter to his mother. But all he got was "You're no looking too well, Major Kinloch. Would ye mind if I had yer lunch?"'

'Yes, I've always loved that story too.' Geordie smiled.

When they reached Newtonmore they turned right along the narrow road to the railway station. It was a simple Highland station with a single track, which happened to be the main line connecting Inverness with Kings Cross. During the war, before their father was sent off to fight in North Africa, he would take all available leave to return here and see his mother. He used to describe how the heavy trains, packed with troops heading northwards and naval shells

132

destined for Scapa Flow, required three locomotives to haul the weight over the Drumochter Pass.

Today, the station was adorned with flower baskets hanging from ornate lamp posts and decorative posters advertising the Highland Line. The trains were colourful three-carriage diesels that skittered with ease between Inverness, Perth and other points north and south. There was no hint of the desperate days of 1942 as the skylarks twittered invisibly, high above the adjacent meadow.

The brothers walked to Dunmore. Their grandmother's house was a small but handsome Victorian lodge set on a ridge among Scots pines with panoramic views of the Spey valley and the hills beyond.

'Nothing much has changed.' Geordie observed.

'It could do with a lick of paint and some work to the roof.' Archie commented.

'Yes, I suppose it is in need of attention. But for all we know it was always thus. We were very young when we used to come here.'

'Maybe, but Gran was really house proud. The brass was always polished and ...don't you remember that smell of furniture wax whenever you entered her house? '

'I do, now you mention it—and how she'd put our toothbrushes out on the window sill to dry in the sun each morning?'

They agreed that Dunmore would never have had a slipped slate or weatherboards in need of fresh paint, back in Those Days.

They drove to the village and turned left off the main street onto a narrow track heading up to the moors. After a mile or so Geordie parked the car and reached behind for the polythene bag.

'Where shall we go?' he asked.

'Let's head for the Calder River and follow it for a while. I'm sure a suitable place will suggest itself'.

They walked in the sunshine along an easy footpath. It led to a bluff overlooking a peaty river sparkling merrily towards the Spey in the valley far below. The Calder's banks were overgrown with willow and alder. A Boy Scout camp was pitched in a meadow below the bluff. Boys were playing volley ball over an improvised net, a boy strummed his guitar outside a heavy green canvas tent anchored by sisal guy ropes secured with wooden pegs. Boys lay reading in the grass, others carried firewood into the camp for their evening sing-a-long.

'This scene is straight out of the 1930's' Archie exclaimed, 'I didn't realize youths in Britain still did this kind of thing.'

'Nor did I. It all seems so unbelievably wholesome.'

They descended into the valley, filed past the Scout camp and followed the Calder downstream. After half a mile the river narrowed into a series of deep pools where, over the eons, storm water had carved wondrous shapes out of the granite. The brothers sat on a boulder overlooking the scene.

'What d'you think about here?' Geordie gestured at the pool below.

'It's as good a place as anywhere.' His brother nodded.

Geordie pulled a heavy mauve plastic container from the polythene bag and wrestled with its wide, heavy screw top. Finally, it eased and came off.

'Here? Sure?'

'Yup, let's do it.'

Geordie poured the ashes into the deep, slow-flowing pool below them. He hadn't given it any forethought, and was surprised to see ash spreading rapidly across the surface like an oil slick, leaving a grey rim on the rocks on the opposite bank.

'Crikey. I imagined they would sink. This is kind of, like, pollution.' Geordie said. 'I hope nobody comes along and sees the mess we've made.'

'Don't worry. The ashes will dissipate as soon as they hit the faster stretch further down,' Archie paused 'Besides, Dad would have loved it here.' He hadn't quite come to terms with his father belonging in the past tense.

After all his plans for a ceremony as he consigned their father's ashes to the Calder River, the moment turned out to be more prosaic than Geordie had anticipated. Archie showed no emotion and it hadn't seemed appropriate to say a prayer. He merely muttered 'Bye Pop' as he emptied the container into the peaty water.

They sat quietly for a few minutes watching the ashes drift downstream and the pollution stain extending gradually with the flow.

'Time for lunch.' Archie broke the spell.

'That's definitely what he would have said.' Geordie laughed. He screwed the solid top tightly back onto the mauve container and slipped it into the polythene bag, much lighter now. The brothers strolled back wordlessly along the Calder and up the bluff to the car.

'What are you going to do with that thing?' Archie asked as Geordie chucked the bag back onto the back seat.

'Haven't thought. I'll probably burn it next time I have a bonfire. Why? Do you want it?'

'No thanks, there's no way I want it. It has terrible gri-gri. It's just that... it should be disposed of thoughtfully, as they say.'

After picking at a greasy unfrozen lunch at a local hotel the brothers headed south. They parted at Perth station, where Archie caught a late afternoon train to London.

Geordie motored home alone in a reflective mood. Tipping his father's ashes into the Calder was as final as it gets, the last set of buffers on the railway line of life. What made him think that his father would have approved? He didn't know. The old man had loved the Scottish Highlands but also had loved the South of France and had been partial to racing at Longchamps . He'd loved the Loire Valley and parts of Normandy, the Bernese Oberland and the Amalfi Coast. He'd also been fond of West Country churches and Walmer Castle too, for that matter.

Committing his ashes to one place was bound to be to the exclusion of other places. Should they have split the ashes into ten parts and scattered a handful at each favourite location? Would the old man's soul have been more at rest if they'd done that? Seeing how his ashes had spread over the water, had throwing them into a peaty Highland river been a mistake? They would have reached the

Spey by now, on the way to the Moray Firth and the North Sea beyond. Perhaps today's effort had had the opposite effect on the old man's soul, by continuing his journey rather than laying him to rest in one spot?

'Naa. The old man would have been delighted that his boys took the trouble to come up with an imaginative place to scatter his mortal remains.' He said aloud as he parked the car in the courtyard at Balnadarg. Still in conversation with himself, Geordie opened the door to the house and slung the polythene bag over a brass hook in the corridor.

There it remained until one blustery afternoon in September. Geordie had amassed a huge pile of undergrowth for a bonfire. For weeks he'd been clearing an invasion of wild rhododendrons from the woods. Random beech, oak and ash branches were also in the pile, the casualties of summer storms that had ripped limbs off many trees around the estate.

He scrunched sheets of newspaper into a ball and built a wigwam of dry sticks over it. He fished into his pocket for a flat book of matches he'd taken from a Minneapolis restaurant years earlier. He struck a match and set fire to a protruding wisp of newspaper. Flames enveloped the paper ball rapidly; dry sticks crackled as the bonfire gained hold. Geordie added larger dry sticks and soon an impressive conflagration was devouring the rhododendron branches and everything else he threw onto the flames.

'It's time for our final farewell.' Geordie said sadly. He stepped back and removed the maroon plastic container from the polythene bag he'd brought out from the house. He glanced at the label for the last time:

Barham Crematorium. Cremation no 112785.
James R E Kinloch. 15th May 2008

'Adieu, old soldier.'

He hurled the container into the heart of the flames. It kept its shape for a few seconds before the thick plastic caught fire and started buckling in the intense heat. As Geordie turned away to find more branches to feed the inferno, an almighty bang ripped through the bonfire as the container exploded. The burning lid whizzed through the air like a flaming frisbee and struck him with tremendous force on the back of his neck. Geordie fell to his knees and sank slowly, face forward, into the forest leaves.